The Healthy Way to Stretch Your Dog

A Physical Therapy Approach

Sasha Foster, *MSPT*

Ashley Foster, *BS, CPDT*

Wenatchee, Washington U.S.A.

The Healthy Way to Stretch Your Dog
A Physical Therapy Approach
Sasha Foster and Ashley Foster

Dogwise Publishing
A Division of Direct Book Service, Inc.
403 South Mission Street, Wenatchee, Washington 98801
509-663-9115, 1-800-776-2665
www.dogwisepublishing.com / info@dogwisepublishing.com
© 2009 Sasha Foster and Ashley Foster

Illustrations: Ashley Foster with exception of Illustrations 2.1-2.17
and 7.2 by Sasha Foster
Photos: Ashley Foster with exception of Photos 3.1–3.15
and B.2 by Sasha Foster
Graphic Design: Lindsay Peternell

Patent-Pending Joint Stabilized Straight Plane Movement Stretching is the proprietary system of Love Dogs. Stretch Dogs. LLC. All Rights Reserved.

All rights reserved. No part of this book may be reproduced or transmitted in any form or by any means, electronic, digital or mechanical, including photocopying, recording or by any information storage or retrieval system without permission in writing from the publisher.

Limits of Liability and Disclaimer of Warranty:

The author and publisher shall not be liable in the event of incidental or consequential damages in connection with, or arising out of, the furnishing, performance, or use of the instructions and suggestions contained in this book.

Library of Congress Cataloging-in-Publication Data
    Foster, Sasha, 1971-
    The healthy way to stretch your dog : a physical therapy approach / Sasha Foster, Ashley Foster.
    p. cm.
    ISBN 978-1-929242-54-2
    1. Dogs--Health. 2. Stretching exercises. 3. Massage for animals. I. Foster, Ashley. II. Title.
    SF427.F74 2008
    636.7'08937182--dc22
                           2008019630

ISBN13: 978-1-929242-54-2
Printed in the U.S.A.

To Diesel, for throwing himself on the floor, and to Serendipity.

Thank you for this opportunity!

CONTENTS

ACKNOWLEDGMENTS

This book would not have been possible without the help and enthusiasm of a large group of human-dog teams. We would like to thank Debbie Garfield and her Irish Setter, Hogan. Hogan was our dog stretch hero in the development of this book but unfortunately he was unable to grace these pages—his magical red feathers made it difficult to see the stretches clearly. Debbie helped in immeasurable ways including bringing Hogan to multiple short-notice photos shoots, helping with set preparations, and thoroughly editing the manuscript prior to submission. A special thank you Ginger Sammonds and her Vizsla, Savannah, for their time and flexibility on so many levels. Ginger was one the first people we called to discuss the stretch method and her support throughout the process has been tremendous. What would we do without her? Thanks to Karlene Brumfield and her beautiful beagle, Puzzle. We are happy to have had the opportunity to capture Puzzle's sweet demeanor in print before she passed away. Thanks to Helen and Chris Holmquist-Johnson and their yellow Lab, Aspen; her kind face warms every page she is on. Thanks to Vicki Harris (Imagemaker Dobes) who entrusted Diesel Foster, the big black boy who started this whole project, to Ashley.

A very special thank you to Debra and Mark Holmes, DVMs, who were supportive of this book from the beginning; Dr. Debra guided the original draft and then took the time to mull over each and every page of the final draft even while her family was home for the holidays. A special thanks to Dr. Mark and all of the Paws crew for their care and compassion during Diesel's cancer treatment. Without Diesel, this book would not be. Thanks to Travis Martin, a great business mentor, who helped inspire the business plan that will allow us to share these stretching technique with the world. Thanks to all of our friends and family whose love and support continues to encourage us to listen to our hearts and follow our dreams.

A deep well of gratitude to Dogwise Publishing who has provided us with kind support and education through the publishing process. We had everything to learn and their expertise turned our fifty-page manual into the beautiful book you see today.

And last but not least, to sisters and best friends who made the choice to allow their relationship to change and grow as the book evolved. For us, the tangible manifestation of this process is this beautiful book; the spiritual one is the love and effort that transformed our lives in the process.

With gratitude,

Ashley and Sasha

FOREWORD

My training as a veterinarian and acupuncturist has opened my eyes to the rapidly evolving world of veterinarian medicine. Massage therapy, chiropractic, acupuncture, herbal medicine, holistic medicine, nutrition, and physical therapy are quickly becoming important complements to mainstream veterinary medicine. When I was first introduced to the concept for *The Healthy Way to Stretch Your Dog*, I was very excited. I realized this could be an important adjunctive tool for veterinarians, veterinary technicians, and pet owners alike.

I have first hand experience of what happens when tissue and muscles and joints are overused and abused. I see many canine patients with muscle tension in their neck, back, triceps, groin, and shoulders. In fact dogs with muscle discomfort and stiffness are often displaying early signs of arthritis. These dogs stretch themselves more, take a little longer to get moving in the morning, and try to take weight off of the painful joint, thereby causing muscle tension and strain in other areas. Proper stretching has become a daily recommendation of mine for many of my canine patients. There is rarely a day that goes by where I don't encounter a patient that would benefit from stretching. A gentle, but consistent, stretching program can truly impact a pet's life. Now, with *The Healthy Way to Stretch Your Dog*, there is a tangible guideline for owners to follow and positively impact the quality of their pet's life.

Finding new ways to help pets live longer, happier lives,

Debra Q. Holmes, DVM, CVA

A NOTE ON SAFETY

While stretching can be extremely beneficial to your dog, there are certain medical orthopedic conditions under which stretching can very harmful. These include but are not limited to hip dysplasia, elbow dysplasia, patellar luxation, anterior cruciate ligament tears, arthritis of any joint including the spine, osteochondrosis dissecans, intervertebral disk disease, wobblers disease of any origin, and other occasionally lameness. Many of these conditions may be "silent," meaning they are not seen when is dog is in his normal environment. However, when the dog is examined by a veterinarian and assessed by specialized orthopedic testing procedures and/or x-rays, there is an indication of the disease being present.

Before beginning this or any other stretching program, we recommend that you consult with your veterinarian. Bring this book with you so your veterinarian can note on the Veterinarian Stretch Screening Form (page 201) which exercises are safe for your dog and which ones should never be used. For example, if your dog has hip dysplasia, your veterinarian may advise you not to use the hip stretching exercises but will encourage you to stretch the spine, neck, and shoulders.

And please do not stretch dogs under 18 months of age. For many dogs, bone growth plates do not completely ossify until this age. Stretching your young dog may put your dog at risk for injury.

The "Attention" Icon

Attention! We do not recommended skimming the text as we feel a thorough understanding of the process of stretching is very beneficial to the quality of the stretches. However, we have provided our readers with a way to quickly access the instructions that are of critical importance to the safety of the dog. The "Attention" icon is used in the text to bring notice to the extreme importance of reading the content in that portion of the stretching instructions. We sincerely thank you for bringing your awareness to this icon throughout the manual.

INTRODUCTION

Years ago, before I was a physical therapist and before I'd met the dog-of-my-life, Quin Foster, I attended dog shows and matches all over the country with my sister Ashley, who was training and showing her dogs in obedience and conformation competition. At that time, I was an aerobic instructor and personal trainer and had received my certifications from national organizations. During my training, I was taught proper techniques and guidelines for exercising, and I also learned quite a bit about stretching. I remember the moment when my vocational training first connected with dog related activities. While attending a national agility trial with my sister, I noticed a woman standing ring side with her dog, lifting the dog's front leg up, and then down. I asked Ashley, "What's she doing to her dog?" She replied very simply, "Stretching." I was inwardly perplexed, since it didn't look right to me—could stretching dog muscle be so totally different from stretching human muscle? If dogs were different…well, the way the woman was doing the stretch might be all right for dogs—I had seen others do it that way, too. But if dogs weren't different, if their muscles worked the same as human muscle, then what she was doing to her dog was exactly the opposite of what I'd been taught. The questioning moment passed and was forgotten over time.

It returned almost ten years later when my sister's Doberman limped into my living room after agility training. For months there had been an uncomfortable area on his upper back. It was so uncomfortable that he had scratched and developed a little bald spot on his shoulder. It seemed to cause more discomfort after large bouts of exercise and that was the case this night. He ran in the house, stopped quickly to scratch his back, rolled on his side, rubbed against the floor, and stood to scratch again. This continued repeatedly. His little itching dance brought him to the living room floor where I was stretching. Diesel threw himself on his side in front of me. I put my hands on him and started to feel the muscles and bones—his scapular retractors

1

tighter on the left than on the right. So I moved his scapula around, relaxing his muscles, and then stretched his front leg towards his head to release the tight muscles on his upper back. His breathing calmed and he sighed a big dog sigh of comfort.

Just then Ashley came around the corner from the kitchen, "What are you doing?" Diesel turned his head to look up at her.

"Stretching his shoulder," as I watched Diesel sit to scratch his back again.

"He's never been stretched that far before. How'd you get his arm extended like that?"

Diesel came back to poke his nose at me.

"Well," I said as I thought about what I'd done, "I just stretched him like I'd stretch a patient."

She sat down on the floor with us. "How did you do it?"

I drew Diesel towards me again as I explained, "His arm goes like that when he's doing agility. It even moves more than that when he's stretching himself."

Diesel put his head on the floor and gave me his leg and I said, "The key is to stabilize the scapula so the muscles around the shoulder can relax." I put my hands back on him, this time thinking about what my PT brain automatically did before. "I find the bones where the scapula meets the humerus and I wrap my fingers around the front of that joint to make it feel stable, then I line his arm bones up with his shoulder joint, then I slowly lengthen the muscles into a stretch." As I did it again, Diesel knew what was happening and he more easily relaxed into the stretch. I held his arm almost parallel to his back again as Ashley watched.

We did this a number of times over the next few months because the stretches seemed to reduce Diesel's desire to itch that one spot and his hair began to grow back. We started stretching all of our dogs and found the process so interesting that we started looking for a book that defined and explained what we were experiencing while stretching our dogs. There was no definitive book. There were some books and DVDs that included stretching, but none integrated some of the most important techniques I'd learned as a PT such as joint stabilization, straight plane movement, and holding a stretch—the techniques that we were using on our dogs with such great results.

As we continued our search for more information, one thing became very clear to us—while there has been a lot of research done recently on stretching for humans which has changed the way we stretch—it hasn't yet changed the way we stretch dogs. In the last thirty years, the research about muscle tissues and the importance of stretching has been applied to the human model so definitively that it has changed the way aerobic participants to elite athletes integrate stretching into their exercise routines. For example, the stretching texts from the 1970's emphasize stretching prior to exercises and they lack specific details about alignment and holding a stretch. The more updated research has shown that lengthening muscle fibers after an event when they are warm and supple improves the quality of the stretch. An improved quality of stretch can decrease the risk of injury to muscles and joints due to repetitive movements or muscle over-use. The research also shows that a stretch must be held for at least 30 seconds to actually lengthen the muscle and connective tissue fibers. Why has this updated information not been integrated into the canine model? Since stretching is truly a valid technique for maintaining joint integrity and muscle health in humans shouldn't we be sharing this with our best friends? The research indicates that human and canine muscle tissue is so similar that dogs should receive the same benefits from stretching that humans do.

The anatomical similarities between human and canine muscle tissues validate the importance of integrating stretching into a canine health model. Although canines are quadrupeds and some of the attachments of the muscles to the bones are different, in general the gross anatomical arrangement is very similar to humans. Of greater significance in confirming the importance of stretching dogs is muscle physiology. Interestingly, the inner workings of muscle cells are very similar in most mammals. When a muscle receives a nerve message and if the appropriate amount of energy is available, it will contract the muscle. As long as the muscle is receiving the message from the nerves, it will continue to contract until it runs out of energy. When the energy is gone, the fibers remain in a contracted, or shortened, position. Muscle tissue that remains in a shortened position over time is prone to injury. This predisposition for injury in fatigued muscle is the reason why all muscle tissue needs to be stretched, human or canine. Stretching returns the muscle tissue to its natural elongated state which improves muscle health and joint integrity.

Our goal in developing this book is to bring the dog world up to date with the importance of stretching and to provide specific techniques for stretching based on the most recent research. By sharing this information with dog owners, we hope to add another preventative/restorative technique to the ever growing list of holistic techniques used to keep our dogs healthy and happy for the span of their lives.

We care for dogs, in part, because they bring us happiness. It is wonderful when we can do something for our dogs that they can't always do for themselves, in this case helping to keep an active dog agile and as pain-free as possible. This affords us an opportunity to bond with these four legged creatures whose mission on Earth sometimes seems to be nothing more than bring us joy—and maybe a sloppy wet tennis ball every once in a while!

Wishing you happy and healthy stretching,

Sasha Foster, MSPT

Chapter 1
CANINE ANATOMY

The techniques outlined in this manual include three important phases for each stretch: joint stabilization; straight plane movement; and the stretch itself. In order to safely and effectively complete each of these phases of a stretch on your dog, general knowledge of joints, muscles, anatomical directions, and joint movements is critical. The illustrations provided in this chapter are meant to introduce some of the concepts and terms that are frequently referred to throughout the manual. A brief introduction here is all that is required since, for each stretch, detailed instructions will be provided that include the joint to be stabilized and the muscles to be stretched.

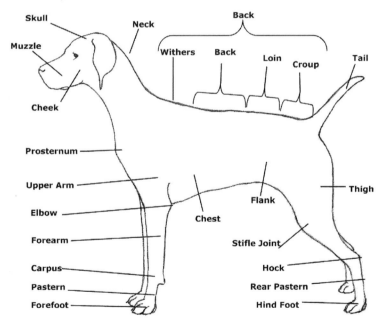

Illustration 1.1. Canine General Structure

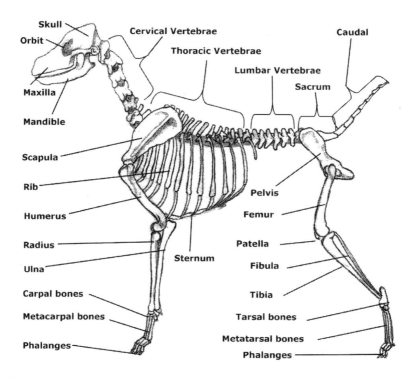

Illustration 1.2. Canine Skeleton

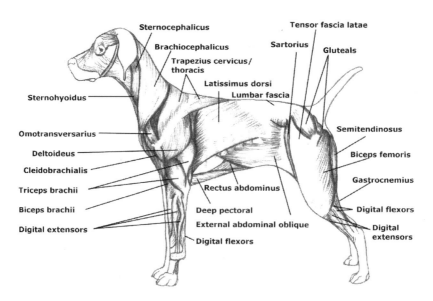

Illustration 1.3. Canine Superficial Musculature Lateral View

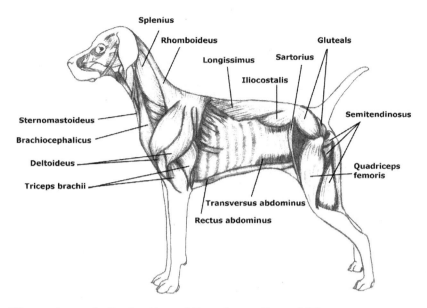

Illustration 1.4. Canine Deep Musculature Lateral View

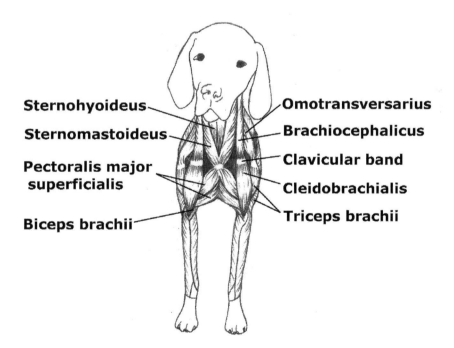

Illustration 1.5. Canine Musculature Anterior View

Lumbar fascia

Gluteals

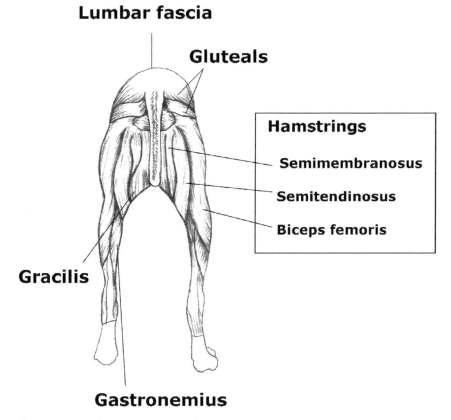

Hamstrings

Semimembranosus

Semitendinosus

Biceps femoris

Gracilis

Gastronemius

Illustration 1.6. Canine Musculature Posterior View

Anatomical Directions

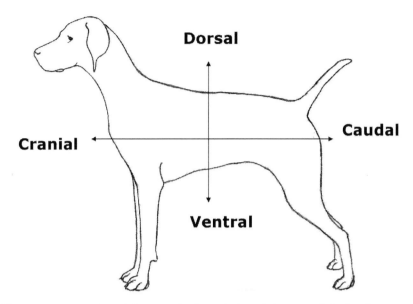

Illustration 1.7. Caudal: *towards the tail;* **Cranial:** *toward the head;* **Ventral:** *underside of the body;* **Dorsal:** *top side of the body.*

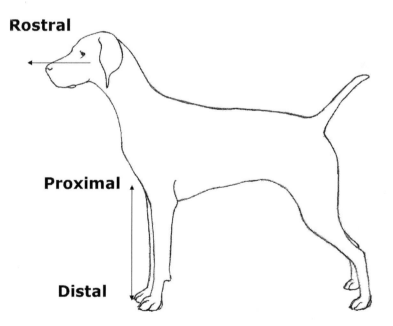

Illustration 1.8. Proximal: *towards the body;* **Distal:** *away from the body;* **Rostral:** *when describing the head, toward the nose.*

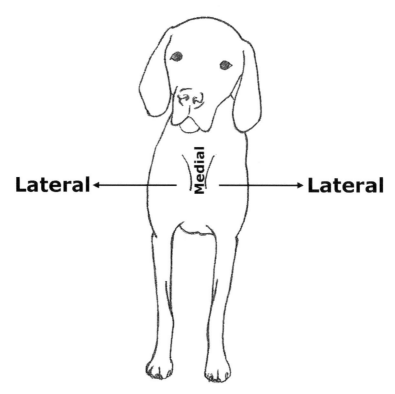

Illustration 1.9. Medial: *towards midline;* **Lateral:** *away from midline.*

Joint Movements

Illustration 1.10. Abduction: *movement away from midline.*

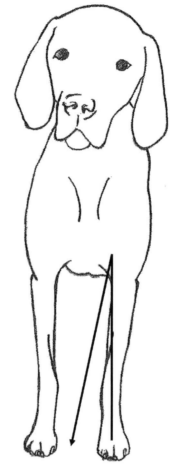

Adduction

Illustration 1.11. Adduction: *movement towards midline.*

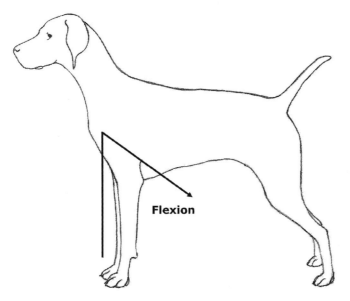

Illustration 1.12. Flexion: *decreasing the angle of a joint.*

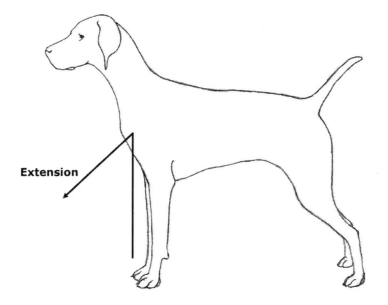

Illustration 1.13. Extension: *increasing the angle of a joint.*

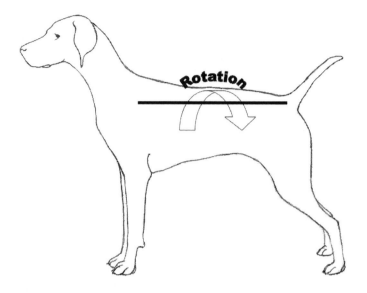

Illustration 1.14. Rotation: *twisting motion around a central axis.*

Chapter 2
WHY STRETCH?

There are two properties a muscle must have to keep the body of a human, a dog, or a cat strong and healthy throughout a lifetime—strength and flexibility.

Muscle strength manifests itself as power. In dogs, that power may be seen in the form of a Sighthound running long distances while lure coursing or it may be in the form of short, quick bursts of speed seen in agility competitions. Starting in an elongated position, the contraction of a muscle creates the power necessary to move the body through space. Just imagine the hind legs of a Greyhound as he runs at full speed. As soon as his hind leg is finished kicking back to propel him forward, it moves forward. This forward movement returns the caudal hip muscles to an elongated position which gives the muscle more power when the leg kicks back again.

When a muscle contracts repetitively over time and is not stretched back to an elongated position, it has a tendency to remain in a shortened position. A good example in humans is the hamstring muscles of long distance runners. If a runner does not fully stretch their hamstrings after a run, over time the hamstrings shorten until the runner will not be able to straighten his knee fully at rest or when running. This can create problems for the muscle and its tendon. Since a muscle creates more power when it starts a contraction from an elongated position, it creates less power if it's starting from a shortened position. If it creates less power, then this begins a cascade of weakness in the muscle that is difficult to overcome if the shortened position of the muscle persists. But the body must still move through space, now with a weakened muscle. The weakened muscle is now trying to do more work from a short-ened position and this is what sets up the parameters for a muscle injury. A muscle that has to do more work than it has the power to do will begin to break down and tear.

A shortened muscle can also cause problems in the joints it surrounds. Muscle tightness around the joint can create uneven pressures through the articular cartilage, the smooth lining that covers the surface of the joints. Uneven pressures can cause uneven wear on this cartilage that over time can lead to degenerative changes inside the joint that will predispose it to arthritis. This painful condition is caused when the cartilage inside the joint wears down leaving only exposed bone. Every time the joint moves, the bone grates against bone causing pain. Stretching can decrease the tightness of the muscle around the joint which allows the pressures inside the joint to remain more even, decreasing the likelihood of degenerative changes in the cartilage over time. This is particularly important for older dogs who are more prone to degenerative changes such as arthritis.

The problems that arise from muscle shortening may likely be prevented with stretching.[1, 2] Stretching is passively lengthening muscle tissue, returning the muscle to its elongated state, thereby maintaining strength and joint integrity. Our dogs instinctively know this. They stretch when they first wake up in the morning or after a long run in the park. And they do the best they can on their own. But, just as Diesel was unable to stretch his scapular retractors by himself, there are many muscles on our dogs that they simply cannot stretch by themselves. They need our help. Using the techniques outlined in this book, we can routinely stretch all the muscles on our dogs as a preventive maintenance measure for life-long wellness. We can also stretch the muscles that support the neck, the scapula, the hip, the stifle—those areas on our dogs that are more prone to over use injuries from highly competitive activities or simply due to aging.

For our dogs to live and age gracefully, it is important to keep up with both muscle properties—strength and flexibility. Keeping our dogs able to engage in activities they enjoy will maintain their strength. Integrating a stretching

---

[1]Pitman, M.I., and Peterson, Lars. *Basic Biomechanics of the Musculoskeletal System*, 2nd Ed., (pp. 106). Baltimore, William & Wilkins, 1989.
[2]Brobeck, J. R. (ed.). *Best & Taylor's Physiology Basis of Medical Practice*, 10th Ed., (pp. 59-113). Baltimore, Williams & Wilkins, 1979.

routine into their care will maintain their flexibility thereby preventing injuries to the muscles and joints. The combination will allow them to be healthy, strong, and flexible throughout the span of their lives.

Stretching Fundamentals

There are five basic principles for safely and effectively stretching your dog. First, the muscles should be **warm** (all bolded terms are included in the Terminology section on page 190). This means you should stretch your dog after taking a walk or engaging in some physical activity. Second, the muscles must be completely **relaxed**. In our canine companions this means we need them to lie down before you begin to stretch them. Third, we must **stabilize the joint** by holding it firmly. When the bones are held correctly it sends a signal to the spinal cord and brain that the joint is secure so the muscles can relax. It also sends a signal to the dog, "You are safe. I have you. You can relax." Fourth, we must stretch the muscles using **straight plane movement**. This means holding the long bones of the limbs in alignment with the joints. This alignment ensures we don't put the wrong pressure through the joint and stretch something we didn't intend to stretch (like the medial ligaments of the stifle). And fifth, the **stretch**. A stretch must be held for 30 seconds to reach both the elastic and non-elastic fibers of the muscle. It is the combination of these fibers that when stretched will decrease the risk of muscle and joint injury for a healthy and pain-free dog life.

The Importance of Warming the Muscle

Research shows that a stretch is safer and more effective on warm muscle tissue. So how should one warm up the muscles? It means exercising for a short period of time to increase blood flow to the muscle tissues before beginning a stretch. Increasing the flow of blood to the muscle tissue does three important things. First, it increases suppleness of muscle tissue, thereby preventing stretching injuries by allowing the muscle fibers to glide against each other more easily. This allows the stretch to reach deep into the fibers of the muscle which is where true stretching occurs. Second, it warms the muscle to allow the elastic tissues to lengthen safely. Just like the elastic in a rubber band, heating elastic makes it less brittle and more likely to lengthen smoothly without disruption to the fibers.[3] Third, it lubricates the joints by decreasing the viscosity of the synovial fluid. Synovial fluid is a matrix of fluid inside a joint capsule that acts a lubricant for smooth joint movement. Warming the muscles decreases the viscosity of this fluid allowing the joint to move more

---

[3]Pitman, M.I., and Peterson, Lars. *Basic Biomechanics of the Musculoskeletal System*, 2nd Ed., (pp. 102). Baltimore, William & Wilkins, 1989.

freely.[4] This in turn allows for a greater range of motion and the ability to stretch more of the muscle fibers. See the illustrations that follow to better picture how these processes work.

Blood Flow Before Exercise

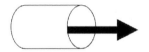

Blood Flow After Exercise

Illustration 2.1. Increasing Blood Flow to the Muscles: *increases suppleness, warms muscle tissue, and lubricates joints.*

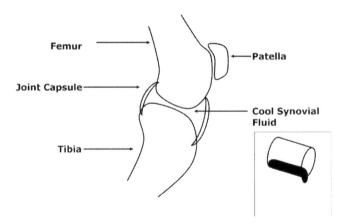

Illustration 2.2. Cool Joint: *when the joint is cool, the synovial fluid is more viscous, making the movement at the joint less fluid.*

---

[4]Mow, V.C., Proctor, C.S., Kelly, M.A. "Biomechanics of Articular Cartilage." Chapter 2: pp. 47-54. *Basic Biomechanics of the Musculoskeletal System*, 2nd Ed. Pitman, M.I. and Peterson, Lars, editors. Baltimore, 1989, William & Wilkins.

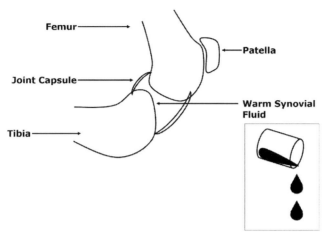

Illustration 2.3. Warm Joint: *When the joint is warm, the synovial fluid becomes less viscous, making the movement at the joint more fluid.*

Warming the muscles and joints is particularly important in older dogs. It is an unfortunate rule of nature that over time elastic tissues lose some of their elasticity.[5] It is also true that over time joint integrity decreases, predisposing our dogs to joint problems. These two underlying issues make warming the muscles extremely important. Since the elastic tissues in the muscles are more brittle and the joints naturally have less movement, warming the tissues will maximize our ability to stretch an old dog and ensure they remain pain-free as we do it. If your old dog shows signs of pain and discomfort during stretching, it may be that their muscles are not yet warm enough. It may also be that there is an underlying pathology that needs to be assessed by your veterinarian. Be very aware of the importance of warming your old dog prior to stretching. A great muscle warming exercise for an older dog is swimming. The water decreases the stresses through the joints while increasing the blood flow to muscles and joints. If water is not easily accessible, a gentle walk for ten to fifteen minutes outdoors or on a treadmill is generally adequate.

The Importance of Relaxation
A muscle must be completely relaxed before a stretch can be safe and effective. If a muscle is not relaxed and you attempt to stretch, you can actually pull a muscle, causing injury to the muscle fibers and connective tissues. The reason is that muscle fibers, or cells, are like combs whose teeth overlap. When the muscle is contracting, the teeth overlap very tightly. If you try to pull on a muscle when it is contracted, you put pressures through the teeth

---

[5]Carlstedt, C.A., and Nordin, M. "Biomechanics of Tendons and Ligaments." Chapter 3. *Biomechanics of the Musculoskeletal System*, 2nd Edition, Pitman, M.I. and Peterson, Lars, editors. Baltimore, 1989, William & Wilkins.

that can cause them to break. If, on the other hand, you allow the muscle to relax, the teeth will just barely overlap, allowing you to lengthen the muscle fibers without risk of injury.

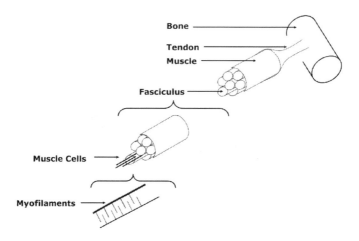

Illustration 2.4. Muscle Tissue: *Muscles are bundles of contracting fibers bound together by connective tissues.*

As seen in Illustration 2.4, deep within the muscle are myofilaments, the contractile units that look like the teeth of a comb. Bunches of myofilaments are bound together to form the muscle cell, or fiber. The fibers are then bound together to form a fasciculus. Many fasiculi are then bound together to form a muscle. The connective tissues that bind the muscle together come together at the end of the muscle to form a tendon which attaches to the bone.

When a muscle contracts, it does so deep down in the myofilaments within the muscle cells which transfers this movement all the way to the tendon, moving the bone so the body can be stabilized or moved through space. When stretching our dogs, we need this entire system from the muscle cell to the tendon to remain relaxed so the tissues will stretch. If we attempt to lengthen the muscle when it has tension, we can pull the muscle fibers causing injury to the tissues.

Stretch the Dog Lying Down
One easy way to keep the muscle relaxed is to have the dog lie down while stretching. Standing or sitting requires muscles to contract to hold the dog in these positions. While standing, sitting, or wiggling out of our grasp, three

different types of muscle contractions are occurring—concentric, eccentric, and isometric contractions[6]—each of which we want to avoid for the stretch to be safe and effective.

A concentric contraction is shortening of muscle fibers. An example is the biceps muscle group on the cranial aspect of your dog's upper arm. When he lifts his paw up to shake your hand, he is concentrically contracting his biceps muscle group.

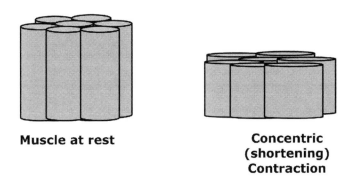

Muscle at rest   **Concentric (shortening) Contraction**

Illustration 2.5. Concentric Contraction: *Muscle fibers shorten.*

During an eccentric contraction, the muscle is lengthening as it contracts. One of the main purposes of eccentric contractions is to decelerate a concentric contraction. Eccentric contractions help to modulate movement to allow for smooth muscle control.

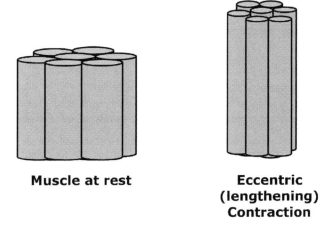

Muscle at rest   **Eccentric (lengthening) Contraction**

Illustration 2.6. Eccentric Contraction: *Muscle fibers lengthen.*

[6]Pitman, M.I., and Peterson, Lars. *Basic Biomechanics of the Musculoskeletal System*, 2nd Ed., (pp. 97-99). Baltimore, 1989, William & Wilkins.

Eccentric contraction occurs, for example, during the lengthening of the quadriceps muscle group (the muscles on the cranial or forward aspect of the dog's back leg), when a dog's legs are reaching back to drive him forward. At the same time, the hamstring muscles on the back of the leg are concentrically contracting to draw the leg to the rear. This simulatneous action means that the muscles on the front of the leg are eccentrically contracting and lengthening to assist with modulating the concentric effort.

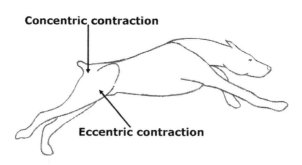

Illustration 2.7. Running Dog: *The muscles on the cranial aspect of the back leg are lengthening as they contract eccentrically to help modulate the movement of the muscles contracting concentrically on the caudal aspect of the back leg.*

During an isometric contraction, the muscle is contracting without shortening or lengthening. Isometric contractions happen all the time to stabilize a joint. An example of an isometric contraction is a dog standing in the conformation ring. The dog is not moving, but the muscles are contracting to hold her up (if they weren't she would fall in a heap on the floor). An example of isometric contractions can be seen in Photo 2.1, on page 23.

Photo 2.1. Isometric Contraction: *The dog is clearly not moving, but the muscles in isometric contraction are clearly visible beneath the coat.*

A stretch is lengthening of muscle fibers and connective tissue when the muscle is at rest.[7] This is why we recommend stretching only when the dog is lying down. In standing, many muscles must contract isometrically to hold the dog in place. The muscles overlap each other throughout the body, so even though it may appear that you are stretching your dog's quadriceps muscle group in standing, in reality it is more likely that you are either stretching only some of the muscles or that you are assisting the dog with an eccentric contraction. In the photos on the next page, notice the difference in range of motion between stretching the shoulder muscles in standing compared to stretching the same muscles in side lying. When the dog is standing, many isometric contractions are required for the dog to stabilize his own body. These contractions decrease the angle and efficacy of the shoulder stretch.

---

[7]O'Sullivan, S. B., "Strategies to Improve Motor Control and Learning," pp. 231, *Physical Rehabilitation Assessment and Treatment.* F.A. Davis, 1988.

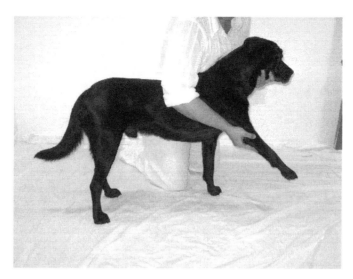

Photo 2.2. Standing stretch: *Notice the isometric contractions beneath the coat, particularly in the hind quarter.*

Photo 2.3. Side lying stretch: *Notice the large difference in the range of motion compared with the stretch in standing. Relaxed muscles allow for this beautiful arc of motion during the stretch.*

Stretch Slowly

Another important way to keep a muscle relaxed for stretching is to move slowly. There are muscle receptors embedded in both the muscle and the tendon are called the **muscle spindle cell** and the **Golgi tendon organ.**

These highly sensitive receptors orchestrate movement by synchronously turning the muscles on and off to either stabilize the body or move it through space. In order to stretch, we want these receptors to remain quiet, allowing us to move the limb without causing the muscles to contract.

Embedded in the muscle fibers is a muscle spindle cell receptor.[8] The purpose of the muscle spindle cell is to tell the spinal cord when a muscle is stretching and at what speed. If a muscle is stretched slowly, then the muscle spindle remains quiet and the muscle will remain relaxed. On the other hand, if a muscle is stretched too quickly, the muscle spindle immediately sends a message through the spinal cord to contract the muscle. This process is known as the **stretch reflex**.[9, 10] Once the muscle has contracted in response to the message, the stretch is being resisted and the stretching process should be started again, this time more slowly.

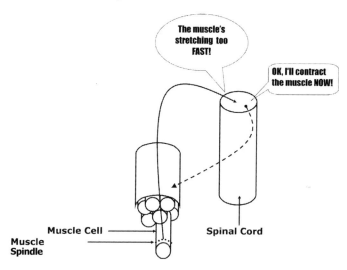

Illustration 2.8. Muscle Spindle: *When a muscle spindle is stretched too quickly, the spindle sends a message through the spinal cord to contract the muscle.*

---

[8]Boyd, I.A., and Smith, R.A. "The muscle spindle." In P.J. Dyck, P.K. Thomas, E.H. Lambert, and R. Bunge, *Peripheral Neuropathy*, Vol 1, Philadelphia, 1984, WB Saunders.

[9]Liddell, E.G.T., and Sherrington, C. "Reflexes in response to stretch." *Proc.Soc. Land. [Biol]* 96:212-242, 1924.

[10]Renshaw, B. "Activity in the simplest spinal reflex pathways." *J. Neurophysiol.* 3:373-387, 1940.

Embedded in the connective tissue of a tendon is the Golgi Tendon Organ receptor. The purpose of the Golgi Tendon Organ is to tell the brain via the spinal cord when the muscle is contracting so it can turn off the opposing muscle group allowing for full movement of the joint.[11] If the muscle is not relaxed, it is contracting, even if the contraction is small. This contraction pulls on the Golgi Tendon Organ that then sends an immediate relaxation message to the opposing muscle group, the group opposite of the muscle you are trying to stretch.[12, 13] If the muscle you are trying to stretch is contracted and the opposite muscle relaxed, begin the stretching process again, this time allowing the stretching muscle to remain relaxed.

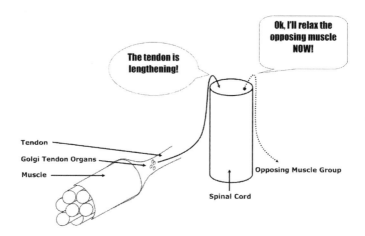

Illustration 2.9. Golgi Tendon Organ: *When a muscle is contracted, the Golgi Tendon Organ will relax the opposing muscle group.*

A general guideline for ensuring the speed of the stretch is slow enough to keep the muscle spindle and Golgi Tendon Organ quiet is the **Three-to-Five Second Rule**. From the limb starting position through the arc of movement until the stretching position is reached, count three to five seconds. The stretch will then be held for 30 seconds. For joints that have larger arcs of movement like the shoulder, hip, neck, and back, the count will be closer to five seconds. For the elbow, stifle, wrist, hock, and feet, three seconds is usually enough.

---

[11]Houk, J.C., Crago, P.W., and Rymer, W.Z. "Functional properties of Golgi tendon organs." *Spinal and Supraspinal Mechanisms of Voluntary Motor Control and Locomotion (Progress in Clinical Neurophysiology 8th Ed.)*, J.E. Desmedt, editor. 1980, Karger.

[12]Houk, J., and Henneman, E. "Responses of Golgi tendon organs to active contraction of the soleus muscle of the cat." *J. Neurophysiology*. 30:466- 481, 1967.

[13]Stein, R. B., and Capaday, C. "The modulation of human reflexes during functional motor tasks." *Trends Neurosci*. 11:328-332, 1988.

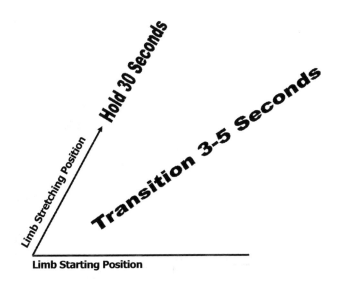

Illustration 2.10. Three-to-Five Second Rule: *From the limb starting position through the arc until the stretching position is reached, count three to five seconds.*

The Importance of Joint Stabilization

Stabilization is the application of a manual force through, around, or over a joint to provide movement control at that joint. When the dog is standing, the force controlling movement at the joint is created by the muscles. When the dog is lying down and relaxed, manual force through our hands must be provided to control the joint movement, otherwise the muscle will automatically contract to manage the movement for us preventing an effective stretch. When a good manual stabilization of the joint is provided, the nerves will remain silenced, the muscle will remain relaxed, and the stretch will be successful.

Joint stabilization is achieved by the placement of the hands as well as by the confidence of the grasp. To safely stretch your dog, you do not have to know the precise details of canine anatomy, but you do need to be aware of the general vicinity of the joint that requires stabilization. For example, when stretching the dog's caudal shoulder, you must place one hand on the scapula while wrapping the fingers of the same hand around the cranial aspect of the shoulder joint. This is the first aspect of stabilization—**hand placement**.

To achieve the second aspect of stabilization apply a **confident grasp**, the manual stabilization of the joint by holding the joint firmly. For the shoulder joint, applying a downward pressure through the scapula with a confident grasp over the shoulder joint provides the nerves with the messages they need to remain quiet. Since the limb is going to move for the stretch, you want to provide the same stabilization the muscles would automatically provide. By providing this stabilization, the spinal cord and brain receive a message that the joint is safely stabilized and the muscles will continue to remain in a relaxed state.

Photo 2.4. Shoulder Stabilization: Hand placement—*place the palm on the scapula. Wrap the fingers around the front of the shoulder and grasp firmly.* **Confident Grasp**—*press down towards the table with the palm. Hold firmly above the elbow with the other hand.*

How much force is needed to stabilize a joint? The amount of pressure needed to keep the muscles relaxed. As a rule, if the muscle is contracted, the stabilization pressure needs to increase. With the correct stabilization pressure, the dog's limb can be moved around by the person stretching the dog without the muscle contracting. In general, for the back, hip, and shoulder, the pressure required is quite high because the joints move in all directions (they bend, twist, extend, and rotate) making them more difficult to stabilize. The joints and bones are also generally larger and heavier, especially in large and giant breed dogs, requiring increased force simply due to size and weight. For smaller dogs, pressure should be applied with the fingers instead of the whole hand. Use enough force, however, to keep the muscles from contracting. Most of the other joints in the fore and hind limbs act as hinge joints—they only bend and extend. This innate stability means less force is required for manual stabilization. For the neck, imagine holding an infant's head—a strong hold with a gentle touch. The combination helps the dog remain relaxed and gives you fairly good control of the stretching movement.

The Importance of Straight Plane Movement

Once your dog is relaxed and you have his joint stabilized, the bones of the joint should be aligned in a straight plane. Straight plane movement means you are lifting the long bones of the limb into alignment with the joint they connect to before, during, and as you stretch. If the bones are not lined up with the joint, it can cause the muscles to contract. It can also cause you to accidentally stretch supporting ligaments (the connective tissues that hold bone to bone) which can predispose the dog to injury.

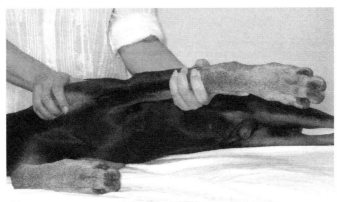

Photo 2.5. Shoulder Straight Plane Movement: *Lift the long bones of the leg into alignment with the shoulder joint.*

Attention! Straight plane movement is particularly important for two joints: the stifle joint and the hip joint. Due to the prevalence of hip dysplasia, patellar luxation, and cruciate ligament tears, both of these joints are at particular risk for injury. Some of these conditions may be "silent" meaning the dog does not show overt signs of pain or lameness. Stretching a dog with an underlying condition can cause permanent injury to the dog. Do not stretch your dog until they have been assessed by your veterinarian. When your dog has been cleared by a veterinarian, please be attentive to both the photos and the instructions. They will show and describe how to maintain a straight plane movement throughout the stretch.

The Stifle Joint

One of the most important joints that require straight plane movement is the stifle joint. The stifle joint is a hinge joint designed to primarily flex and extend. The stifle joint requires particular attention because the hinge-like structure of the bones, muscles, and ligaments makes the patella and cruciate ligaments especially vulnerable to injury if this joint is not properly aligned before stretching.

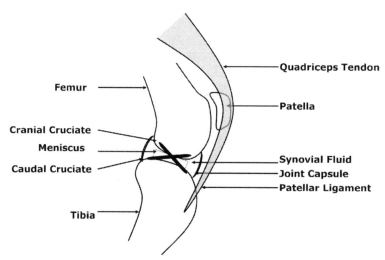

Illustration 2.12. Stifle Joint, lateral view: *The patella, or knee cap, is a small bone that is embedded in the tendon of the quadriceps muscle group on the cranial aspect of the stifle joint. Its purpose is to create smooth movement of the joint. The cruciate ligaments hold the femur and tibia together providing necessary stability to the joint.*

What is the patella? It is a small bone on the cranial aspect of the stifle joint that allows the stifle to flex and extend with mechanical efficiency. Commonly called the "knee cap," the patella is embedded in the tendon of the quadriceps muscle group. Since the patella is embedded in the tendon, stretching the cranial aspect of the hip or stifle will naturally pull on the patella. (The quadriceps muscle group in which the patella is embedded crosses both the cranial hip and the stifle. When you stretch one joint, this anatomy dictates that you actually stretch both joints.) This arrangement is anatomical and cannot be avoided. What must be avoided, though, is putting a medial or lateral force through the patella that will cause a patellar luxation or make an underlying luxation worse. Patellar luxation is when the patella is displaced from its position on the front of the stifle joint to either the medial or the lateral side of the joint. When this happens the mechanics of the knee no longer work correctly causing the dog pain and creating abnormal movement patterns.

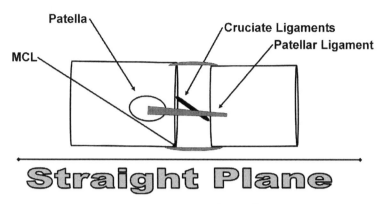

Illustration 2.13. Correct Alignment of the Stifle Joint: *When the stifle joint is held in a straight plane during a stretch, the patella, patellar ligament, cruciate ligaments, and medial collateral ligament are in correct alignment. There is no risk for injury.*

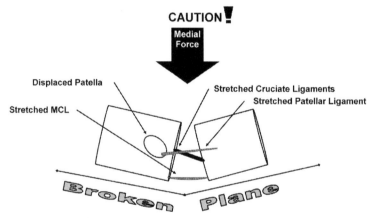

Illustration 2.14. Medial Force, Incorrect Alignment of the Stifle Joint: *When the stifle joint is held in a broken plane during a stretch, the patella, patellar ligament, cruciate ligaments, and medial collateral ligament are stretched out of correct alignment. This puts the patella at risk for luxation and the cruciates at risk for tears.*

All dogs must be evaluated and cleared by their veterinarian prior to doing any stifle stretches. It is critically important that your veterinarian assesses the stability of the stifle before stretching. Stretching an unstable joint may cause permanent injury to your dog. For dogs that have been cleared by a veterinarian for stretching, the following method is a great way to ensure that the stifle joint is aligned and that lateral or medial forces are not being applied to the joint while stretching.

Attention!

Another anatomical aspect of the stifle that requires detailed attention to straight plane movement are the cruciate ligaments. These ligaments support the stability of the stifle joint by holding the tibia in alignment with the femur. Injury to these ligaments can cause pain and immobility. But it is important to be aware that a dog may have "silent" or subclinical strains, sprains, or even tears of the cruciate ligaments. Stretching a dog with an unstable joint or a subclinical condition may cause permanent injury to your dog. For dogs who have been cleared by their veterinarian for stifle stretches, Photo 2.6 is an excellent example of straight plane alignment of the stifle joint.

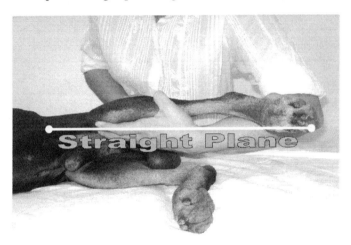

Photo 2.6. Stifle Joint Straight Plane Movement: *Lift the long bones of the leg into alignment with the hip joint. Support the limb in this position by cradling the stifle in your palm and resting the lower leg over your forearm. This position places the femur in alignment with the hip joint, the tibia in alignment with the stifle joint, and the hock in alignment with the joints in the foot. Maintaining this position throughout the stretch as indicated prevents improper forces impacting the joints and ensures safe and effective stretching.*

The Hip Joint
Another important joint that requires proper long bone to joint alignment for straight plane movement is the hip joint. The hip joint is a ball and socket joint that allows for movement throughout a rotational range. The most proximal aspect (the top) of the femur bone, the ball, sits securely into the socket of the pelvis and is held in place by tough ligaments and by the tendons that cross the joint. The ball moves easily in the socket due to the smooth articular cartilage that lines and cushions both the ball and the socket.

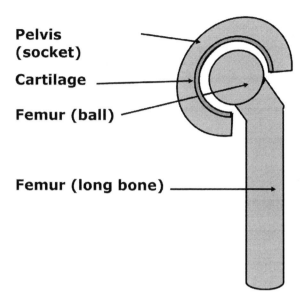

Pelvis (socket)

Cartilage

Femur (ball)

Femur (long bone)

Illustration 2.15. Healthy Hip Joint: *The ball of the femur fits securely in the socket of the pelvis. The articular cartilage is smooth.*

The importance of stabilizing the hip joint and stretching only in a straight plane cannot be stated often enough. This is due to the high prevalence of hip dysplasia, especially in large and giant breeds. Hip dysplasia is a defect in the structure of the ball and socket making the joint prone to erosion of the articular cartilage which causes pain, abnormal movement, and at its worst, subluxation of the hip. There are different grades of hip dysplasia that put a dog at lesser or greater risk for arthritis or degenrative joint disease.

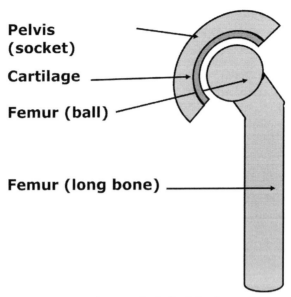

Pelvis (socket)

Cartilage

Femur (ball)

Femur (long bone)

Illustration 2.16. Hip Dysplasia: *The ball of the femur does not fit securely into the socket of the pelvis. The cartilage is grainy, pitted, worn, or torn.*

Attention! When stretching the muscles that surround the hip joint, the ball must move correctly around in the socket. If your dog has hip dysplasia in any form (or underlying arthritis which is common in older dogs), stretching the hip can cause pain, discomfort, or at its worst, subluxation of the hip joint. For this reason we recommend having your dog's hip joints screened by your veterinarian prior to doing any stretches on the hip. If your dog's hips have been cleared by a veterinarian for stretching, we recommend the following technique for ensuring proper stabilization and straight plane movement.

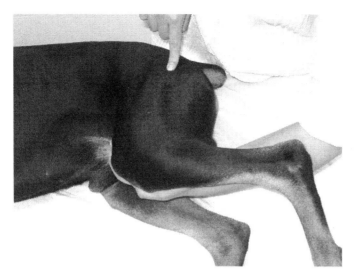

Photo 2.7. Find the Hip Joint: *Feel for the top of the femur bone at the greater trochanter. Note the position of the lower arm supporting the stifle, tibia, and hock.*

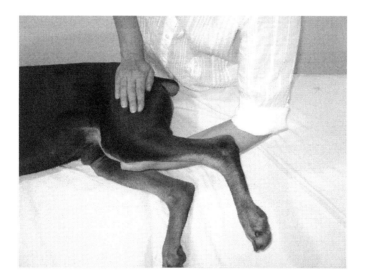

Photo 2.8. Joint Stabilization: *Place the palm of the hand firmly over the greater trochanter. Apply a comfortable downward pressure until the leg relaxes into the supporting arm. Place the other hand between the legs and hold the medial stifle joint firmly (avoid putting your hand on the patellar ligament). Allow the leg to rest on your forearm.*

Photo 2.9. Straight Plane: *Lift the long bones of the limb into alignment with the hip joint. Support the leg with your palm and forearm. Maintain this straight plane position throughout the stretch.*

When stretching dogs, be constantly attentive to the importance of straight plane movement, particularly for the stifle and the hip. Due to the anatomical structure of these joints and their prevalence for cruciate ligament injury, luxation, and dysplasia respectively, straight plane movement is of critical importance. Not only does correct alignment prevent pain and injury in these joints and others, it also ensures the correct muscles are being stretched. When the correct muscles are being stretched in the safest possible ways, the joints and muscles receive the extraordinary benefits of a proper stretch.

The Importance of Holding the Stretch

The properties of muscle fibers, tendons, and ligaments are what determine the length of time a stretch is held. The properties of the fibers and tissues are defined by specific proteins, collagen and elastin, that exist both within and surrounding the muscle tissue. The properties are also defined by how these proteins are arranged. The type of protein and its arrangement determine if the tissue is elastic, partially elastic, or not elastic at all. When stretching a muscle, we want to stretch all three of these tissues. As you can imagine, stretching elastic tissue is pretty easy. Much of the muscle itself is made of elastic tissues. But the muscle fibers are also surrounded by partially elastic and non-elastic tissues that come together at the end of the muscle to form the tendon.[14] It is important when stretching that we stretch the tendon as well as the muscle. In order to stretch these less elastic tissues, a stretch must be held for at least 30 seconds.

---

[14]Carlstedt, C.A., and Nordin, M., "Biomechanics of Tendons and Ligaments," Chapter 3. *Basic Biomechanics of the Musculoskeletal System, 2nd Ed.,* Pitman, M.I. and Peterson, Lars, editors, Baltimore, 1989, William & Wilkins.

Initially during the stretch, there is little resistance as the elastic fibers of the muscle lengthen. As the stretch continues, the elastic fibers become fully elongated and the partially elastic and non-elastic fibers of the tendons and other supporting structures begin to stretch. This is the point at which a slight resistance to the stretch can be felt, and where the stretch should be held for 30 seconds. Holding the stretch for 30 seconds allows the fibers to return to their natural state, thereby decreasing joint pressure and improving the integrity of the joint and the muscles surrounding it. A stretch for less time will lengthen the elastic tissues only, but those tissues generally return to their natural state. (Tissue elasticity decreases with age and is a good reason to stretch the aging dog.) It is the tighter partially elastic and non-elastic tissues that should be stretched to maintain healthy muscles and joints. We can ensure these tissues are being stretched by holding the stretch for 30 seconds at the point in the range of motion where mild resistance is felt.

In Review

Stretching is an important aspect of maintaining your dog's muscle and joint integrity. If done correctly it can be safe and effective while providing an opportunity to bond with your dog. There are five key points to remember as you prepare to stretch your dog.

1. **Warm-up.** Increasing the blood flow to the muscles heats the tissues and lubricates the joints for stretch efficacy, injury prevention, and increased joint range of motion.

2. **Relaxation.** The key to an effective stretch is relaxation of the muscle. To ensure relaxation, have the dog lie down and as you stretch them, move slowly.

3. **Joint Stabilization.** Stretching should be smooth and easy. To keep the muscles relaxed, stabilize the joint manually. Manual stabilization is achieved with correct hand placement and confident grasp.

4. **Straight Plane Movement.** Straight plane movement means lining the long bones of the limbs up with the joints. Straight plane movement ensures you are stretching the muscles you want to stretch instead of connective tissues you don't want to stretch.

5. **Stretch and Hold.** A stretch needs to be held for 30 seconds to lengthen both the elastic and non-elastic fibers. It is the lengthening of both types of fibers that prevents injury and maintains joint integrity.

Chapter 3
DOG BEHAVIOR DURING STRETCHING

Knowing and understanding your dog's behavior and means of communication will improve your ability to effectively stretch your dog. A dog's communication is mostly silent, but they do communicate and they do so quite well. While preparing to stretch and while stretching your dog, pay attention to what they are telling you, as well as to what you are telling them through your body language. Place all of your attention and focus on your dog while you are stretching. Being present, attentive, and calm are comforting signals to your dog which will lead to relaxation and, in turn, make the stretching process easier. Being aware of the non-verbal communication occurring between you and your dog during stretching lets you make subtle changes to your hand placements and stretches, allowing your dog to maintain his comfort level and achieve an effective stretch.

It is important to remember that most dogs have not been formally stretched before. They need time and practice to understand what you are doing. Much of what you are doing in order to stretch your dogs require that they surrender their physical bodies to your trusting hands. They must learn to trust that you will work with them slowly and gently, while teaching them what you are doing is safe and feels good.

Forcing your dog to tolerate stretching might seem to get the job done, but the truth is that if your dog is not relaxed, you are not achieving an effective stretch, nor are you doing anything beneficial for your relationship. If at any time your dog seems distressed, even slightly, you should back up and first teach them to accept being handled prior to starting a stretching routine. If you have any underlying behavior concerns about your dog, seek help from a reward-based trainer or behavioral consultant prior to starting a stretching routine. This chapter provides step-by-step instruction on how to teach your dog to trust you so he can learn to enjoy a good stretch.

Communicating with Your Dog

There are two important ways to communicate with your dog while preparing to stretch.

1. Be Aware of Your Body

A dog must be relaxed in order for you to stretch him effectively. Evaluate your own emotional state prior to stretching. Make sure you are relaxed and calm before you begin. If you are feeling rushed or stressed, your dog will sense it. Use deep breaths and sighs, both act as calming signals to the dog, and he should begin to relax and settle down. Once the dog is on the table, you can quietly place your hands on his sides and take some nice deep breaths before beginning the first stretch.

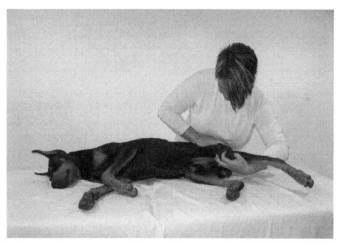

Photo 3.1. Leaning Over the Dog: *Many stretches require leaning over the dog—a hip stretch, for example.*

It is also important to realize that some of the body positions required for stretching may feel threatening or intimidating to some dogs. The best example of this is leaning over your pet since it is the most commonly used position for stretching your dog. Some dogs may perceive leaning over (looming) as a threatening or intimidating posture and, as a result, they will be very uncomfortable. If your dog does not feel comfortable with you leaning over them, they probably will not appreciate a stretch. In a case like this, a professional reward-based trainer may help you resolve this issue. Please don't try to force your dog to allow you to lean over him. It will be uncomfortable, possibly dangerous, and fruitless for both of you.

Stretching requires that your dog be able to relax into your hands no matter the position of his body or the placement of your hands. But not all dogs can do this. They have their own histories and their own little quirks and it is our job as humans to be aware of those quirks and gently work through them or ask for professional assistance if we can't work it out ourselves. Here are a few other things that might make some dogs feel uncomfortable:

- lifting them onto the table

- lying on their side

- touching and holding of the feet, limbs, and head

2. Be Aware of the Dog

Always be aware of your animal. Dogs are excellent communicators, but humans typically don't pay attention to their subtle, mostly silent cues. If your dog exhibits any of the following behaviors while you are preparing to stretch or are actively stretching, you should stop immediately and give the dog a rest: *rigid body, shaking, excessive panting, pawing, kicking, showing the whites of their eyes, yawning, licking their nose, or squirming*. Your dog is trying to communicate with you that they are feeling stress, pain, or fear. And if your dog *growls or snarls*, definitely stop stretching! If any of these occur, it is recommended that you consult a veterinarian to rule out any possible medical reasons and/or a professional reward-based trainer to assist you with behavioral modifications.

Getting On and Off the Table

The stretches in this book are shown on a table but also may be done on the floor. If using the table, please be aware that many dogs are leery of getting onto high surfaces. If your dog is resistant, it's important to take your time teaching him that getting on the table is safe and fun. Practice short sessions of getting on the table, eating a few goodies, and then assisting them off the table. When they are getting on and off the table with ease, begin teaching them how to lie down on the table.

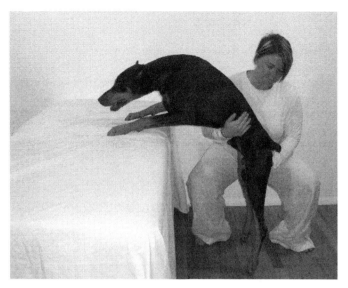

Photo 3.2. Getting on the table: *The table is a good thing! We do not encourage having your dog jump up or down from the table on his own due to the possible risk of injury. Encourage him to place his front two feet on the table while you lift his back end.*

Photo 3.3. Lifting off the table: *Notice how I wait for Diesel to lean into me before lifting him off the table.*

Photo 3.4. Lifting off the table: *When getting off the table, help to lower your dog to the floor. Remember to bend your knees while keeping your back straight!*

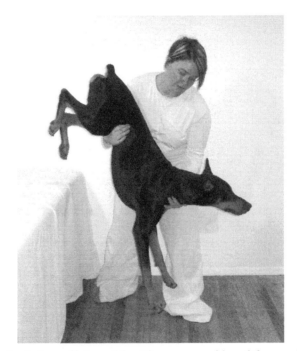

Photo 3.5. Assisting off the table: *If you are unable to lift your dog off the table, assist him by placing one arm around his chest and the other under his flank. As he comes off of the table, you can lighten his landing and ensure that he does not slip.*

Lying Down on the Table

Lying down on the table or floor is vital to the safety and relaxation of your dog during stretching. Again, take your time teaching your dog that lying down on the table on his own is fun and rewarding. When the dog can comfortably lie down on the table, begin teaching contact comfort. Don't forget to utilize deep breaths to aid in your dog's relaxation.

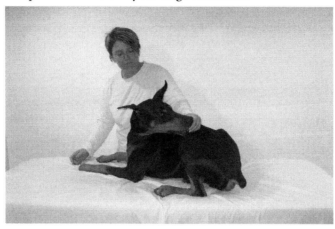

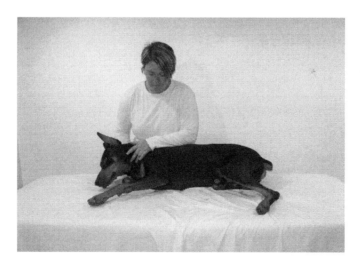

Photos 3.6 and 3.7. Lying down on the table: *Once on the table, have him lie down on his side. Be aware that a large or giant breed dog requires more table space to lie down on his side, you need to assist him in positioning himself properly, so falling off is not an additional worry. Please don't force your dog into this position. If needed, use a tasty treat to help him into the position as shown here. And don't forget to reward him with it once he lays himself down!*

Teaching Contact Comfort

It is important for the dog to learn to relax and enjoy stretching if it is going to be beneficial. Teaching your dog **contact comfort** (the idea that he will associate your contact with him with pleasure) will make him easy to handle, but also offers a great animal/human bonding experience.

Recommendations before beginning:

1. Assess your own emotional state—are you relaxed? Take some deep breaths to communicate your relaxed state to your dog.

2. Assess your environment—is it quiet, calm, free of distractions?

3. Always let your dog know where you are by keeping one hand on his body. Quietly move from one area of the body to the other, keeping constant hand to dog contact, while working on these exercises.

4. For particularly sensitive areas, quietly touch the area with one hand while allowing the dog to nibble on a treat held with the other hand. Do this before actually begining the stretch, this is just to get the dog to associate being touched in sensitive area with good things, in this case, a treat.

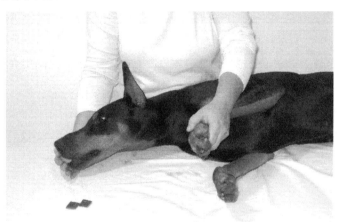

Photo 3.8. *Diesel nibbling on a treat while his foot is touched.*

5. If at any time your dog gets stressed by your touch and movement, back up to the previous step. Continue the contact comfort at this level until you're both comfortable. Quit on a high note and start again tomorrow.

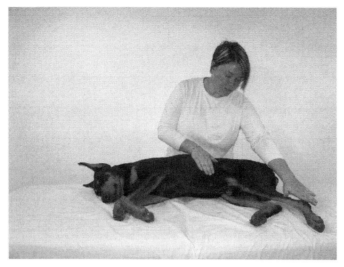

Photo 3.9. Contact Comfort I: *With your dog lying on his side, begin stroking him from his ears to his tail. Continue stroking him until he is settled into your touch and relaxed.*

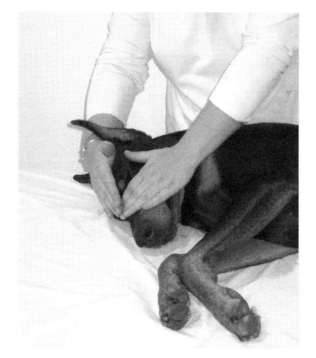

Photo 3.10. Contact Comfort II: *Move to the head and gently stroke all over the face—continue until he is relaxed.*

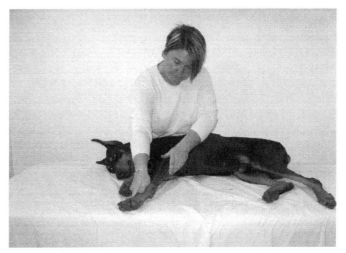

Photo 3.11. Contact Comfort III: *Quietly move to the legs. Begin by giving long strokes from the point of the shoulder/hip to the feet.*

Photo 3.12. Contact Comfort IV: *Progress to the feet. Hold the foot with one hand, while gently touching the foot all over with the other. Once the dog settles into the gentle touch, begin to gently separate the toes and touch them on all sides.*

Once your dog remains relaxed and comfortable while you move your hands all over their body, begin teaching joint stabilization.

Teaching Joint Stabilization

In order for the muscle to remain relaxed while stretching, the joint must be stabilized. This means you must hold the bones above and below the joint firmly and securely. It also means your dog must be relaxed and comfortable while you are stabilizing the joint. Take your time teaching your dog what joint stabilization feels like by repeating the following techniques until the dog remains relaxed while you stabilize his joints.

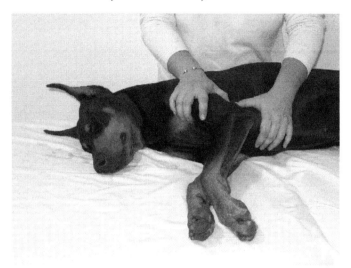

Photo 3.13. Hand Placement: *Once he relaxes, begin locating the proper bones for correct hand placement to ensure joint stabilization.*

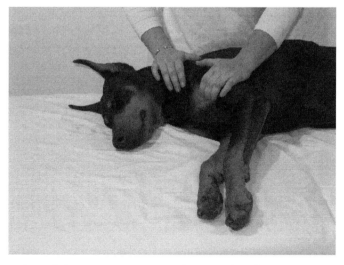

Photo 3.14. Stabilization Pressure: *When your hands are in the proper place, apply a small amount of downward pressure, and release. Repeat until the dog remains relaxed with this pressure.*

A Stretch Question

Q: How much force is needed to stabilize a joint?

A: The amount of pressure needed to keep the muscles relaxed. As a rule, if the muscle is contracted, the stabilization pressure needs to increase. With the correct stabilization pressure, the dog's limb can be moved around by the person stretching the dog without the muscle contracting.

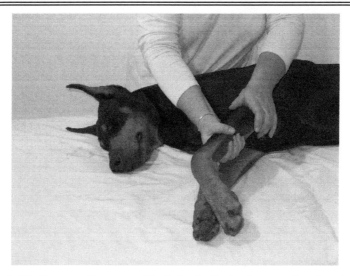

Photo 3.15. Squeeze Pressure: *Encircle the limb with your hand and apply a slight squeeze and then release. Repeat until the dog accepts the pressure from above the elbow down the limb to directly above the foot.*

In Review

Stretching should be enjoyable and safe for both you and your dog, so be aware of both you and your dog's state of mind. Don't just rush into it and be willing to stop if need be. If your dog is uncomfortable with any of these basics—getting on the table, laying down on the table, contact comfort, or joint stabilization—just take a step back and give your dog a break. At first he won't know what you're doing to him and it can be frightening. If you take slow and easy steps, he will learn to be comfortable. You will be creating a safe and relaxing atmosphere for both of you. Once he is comfortable with these things and is melting into your hands, then move to the stretching itself.

Photo 3.16. *An example of a calm and relaxed dog!*

Chapter 4

THE SET-UP

Keeping your own body relaxed is of primary importance when stretching your dog. The best way to do this is to have the correct set-up. It should be comfortable for you and this comfort is in turn is communicated to the dog by your body language. We recommend four different set-ups to allow you to safely stretch your dog at home or ring-side: standing; chair sitting; floor sitting; and kneeling.

The human spine needs to remain in a neutral position for the muscles, tendons, and ligaments to work the way they are designed to work. Any other position will put additional stresses on the back and will predispose your body to injuries. A neutral spine means the natural **lumbar lordosis**, or curve, is maintained. No matter which set-up you choose, you should always maintain lumbar lordosis to ensure you aren't putting undo stresses on your back.

Standing
The safest set-up for both you and your small or large breed dog is an adjustable height massage table. Before the dog gets on the table, set the table to a height that places the dog at about your waist height when he or she is lying on the table. At first this position may seem quite high, especially if you are used to giving dog massages. This is higher than what is generally recommended for massage for important mechanical reasons. Massage requires application of mechanical pressures into muscle tissues. It is more efficient to place the table a bit lower so you can use your body weight to help apply the pressure, thus decreasing the stresses on your own muscles and joints. Stretching is a

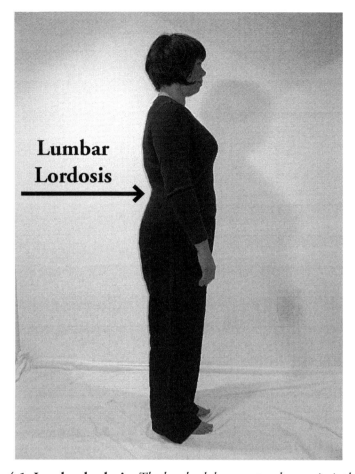

Photo 4.1. Lumbar lordosis: *The low back has a natural curve in it that should be maintained while stretching your dog.*

bit different in that we are moving a limb through a straight plane and we are then holding it…for 30 seconds. If the table is too low, the stress on the low back while holding the limb for 30 seconds can be quite high. If you find your low back is bothering you while you are stretching your dog, raise the table a little more until you find a position that is comfortable for you.

Once the table height is right for you, make sure you place the dog very close to the front of the table—the closer to the front of the table, the less stress on your back. It may take a few trials to get your dog to feel comfortable there. To help them get comfortable, stand close, right up against the table. Leaving no space between the edge of the table and your body, will make the dog feel more secure.

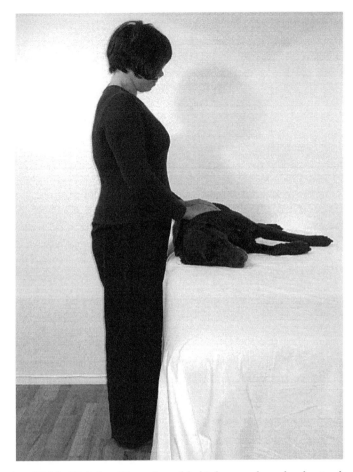

Photo 4.2. Table Height: *Place the table high enough so the dog is about your waist height when he is lying on the table. This position allows you to maintain lumbar lordosis throughout the stretch. Place the dog close to the front of the table so you don't have to bend over.*

If you have weak back muscles or a back problem, a great way to decrease the stress in your low back is to place a low stool under one of your feet beneath the table. By putting your foot up on the stool, you are tilting your pelvis in a way that decreases painful forces through your back. Be aware of the shoes you are wearing, low or no heel is highly recommended.

Sitting in a Chair

Alternatively, if you know your back can be painful in standing, adjust the height of the table to a lower position, and sit in a chair next to the table to stretch the dog. This is an excellent position for small breeds. It is also an excellent position if you don't have a massage table. Many standard grooming tables are an appropriate height for stretching while seated.

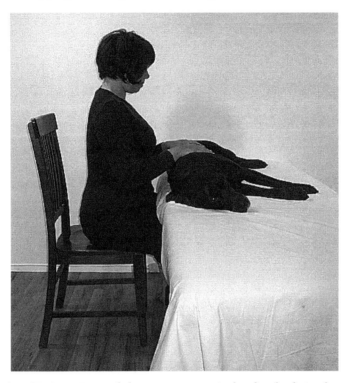

Photo 4.3. Sitting: *Even while sitting, maintain lumbar lordosis, the natural spinal curvature.*

Sitting or Kneeling on the Floor

We understand that in the real world most people do not have massage tables. If you need to stretch your dog in an environment where tables, grooming or otherwise, are not available, stretching on the floor is a viable option, just try to maintain a neutral spine. If your dog is participating in conformation and his grooming must be maintained, a stretching mat may be used.

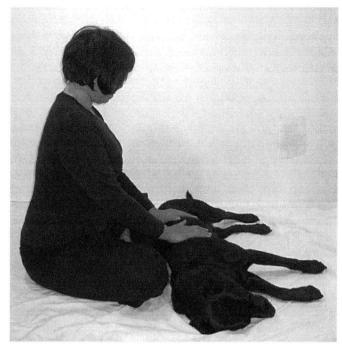

Photo 4.4. Floor sitting: *Maintain lumbar lordosis.*

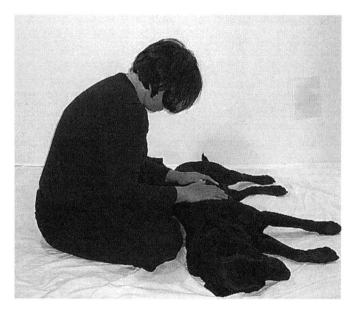

Photo 4.5. Incorrect position: *The low back is rounded putting increased pressure through the low back.*

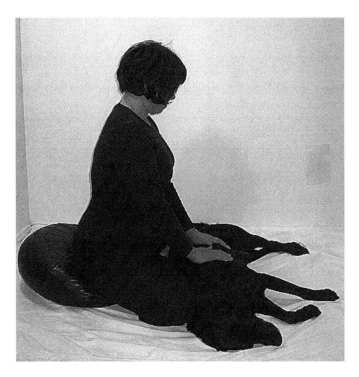

Photo 4.6. Floor sitting with cushion: *If you cannot keep a neutral spine in these positions, it usually means your hamstring muscles are tight. Try sitting on a cushion to maintain lumbar lordosis.*

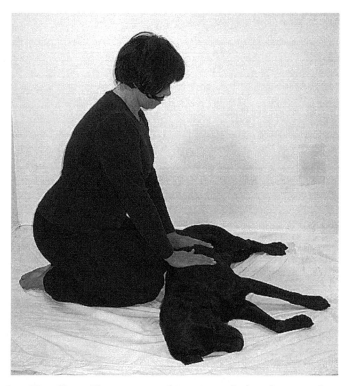

Photo 4.7. Kneeling: *If you are stretching ring side, kneeling may be an option. Be cautious of how your knees feel—if you feel tightness or pain, do not attempt stretching in this position.*

Working with the correct set-up protects our own bodies, especially our backs. Secondarily, the dog feels secure and safe when we feel stable and secure. The dog can sense our pain/tension, and react by not fully relaxing himself. If the set-up is comfortable for both, the experience will be positive and rewarding and the stretch will be safe and effective for both.

Chapter 5
FORELIMB STRETCHES

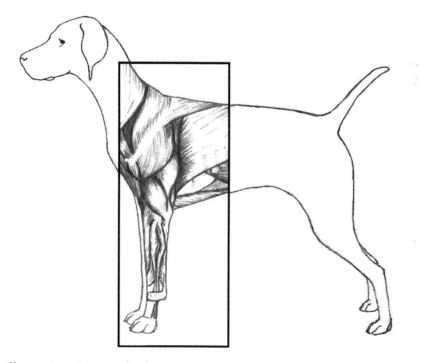

Illustration 5.1. Forelimb

The forelimb, or front leg, of the dog consists of the shoulder, elbow, carpus (wrist), pastern, foot joints, the muscles and tendons that move them, and the supportive ligaments. The shoulder is a ball and socket joint allowing for a large range of motion. The elbow joint is a hinge joint that can flex and extend. The carpus, pastern and the foot joints are extremely complex joints that can move in many different directions. The biomechanics of these joints work together to carry more than half a dog's body weight and to absorb forces created during movement. Because of the biomechanics, the muscles that move the joints can become tight predisposing a dog to pain and injury in the forelimb. Stretching is an excellent way to maintain muscle health and prevent injuries.

Attention! There are a number of forelimb diagnoses including osteochondrosis dessicans (OCS) and elbow dysplasia that can be exacerbated with stretching. If your dog has one of these diagnoses or demonstrates signs of pain in the forelimb, consult your veterinarian for stretch recommendations.

The Shoulder[1]

In general, the more flexibility or range of motion a joint has during regular activities, the more the muscles surrounding the joint are prone to tightness due to overuse. (If a joint is very flexible, the muscles have to work very hard to control the movement at the joint.) This is particularly true of the shoulder joint. The shoulder joint is a ball and socket joint; the ball is the head of the humerus and the socket is in the edge of the scapula. The scapula is then connected to the ribs, not by joints, but by muscles only. Any time the front limb of the dog moves, the muscles that hold the scapula to the body must contract to either stabilize the scapula or to move it. In other words, unless the dog is lying down, the muscles of the scapula are always hard at work. If these hard working scapula muscles become overworked, it can be difficult for a dog to stretch on his own.

Attention! Due to the high level of mobility of the scapula, it is crucial to securely stabilize the scapula prior to stretching by pressing it firmly against the rib cage. This firm stabilization sends the message to the muscles that they can relax. Once they do, the stretch can be effective.

A Stretch Question

Q: How do I know if I'm providing enough stabilization?

A: As a rule, if the muscle is contracted, the stabilization pressure needs to increase. With the correct stabilization pressure, the dog's limb will completely relax into your hands and will be floppy. When the limb is relaxed like this, it can be moved around without causing the muscles to contract. It may take some practice to achieve the appropriate level of stabilization to keep your dog's limb relaxed. If your dog won't relax it may be a sign something is wrong, always have your dog cleared by a veterinarian prior to beginning stretching.

---

[1]For the purpose of this book, we will use the terms "shoulder flexion" and "shoulder extension" as they apply to movement in humans. In veterinary clinical terms, shoulder flexion is movement of the humerus in the caudal direction; shoulder extension is movement of the humerus cranial direction.

Shoulder Flexion Stretch

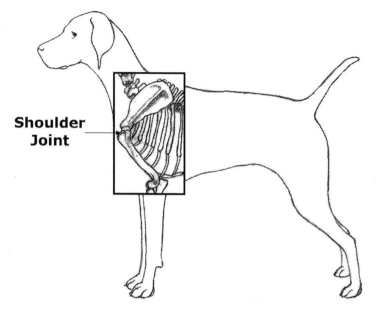

Illustration 5. Stabilized Joint: *The Shoulder Joint (The Glenohumeral Joint).*

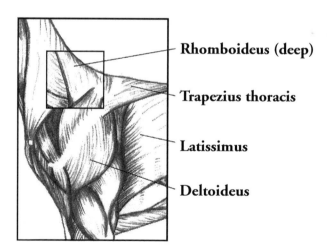

Rhomboideus (deep)

Trapezius thoracis

Latissimus

Deltoideus

Illustration 5.3. Muscles To Be Stretched: *Latissimus dorsi, Deltoideus, Rhomboideus, Trapezius thoracis.*

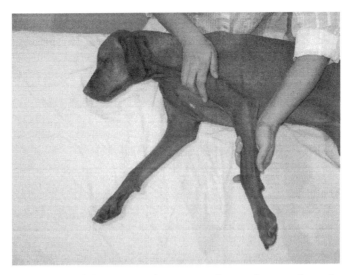

Photo 5.1. Joint Stabilization: *Place your palm on the scapula and wrap the fingers around the cranial aspect of the shoulder joint. Firmly press your palm downward towards the ribs. Hold beneath the elbow with the other hand.*

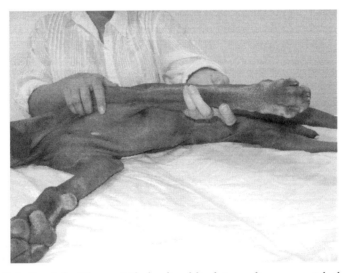

Photo 5.2. Straight Plane: *Lift the distal limb into alignment with the shoulder joint creating a straight plane.*

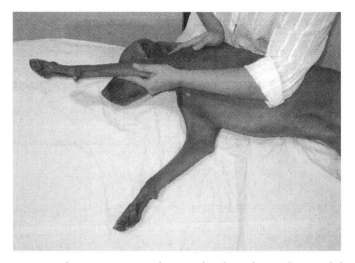

Photo 5.3. Stretch: *Maintaining the straight plane, begin the stretch by reaching the elbow forward allowing it to straighten as the leg reaches forward. The scapula will naturally rotate beneath the stabilizing hand in the direction of the stretch. Allow this scapular rotation, continuing to press downward towards the ribs. Continue to reach the leg forward until feeling a slight resistance. Hold for 30 seconds.*

Photo 5.4. Small dog stretch: *For smaller dogs, fingers are adequate to maintain joint stabilization, straight plane, and stretch.*

Shoulder Extension Stretch

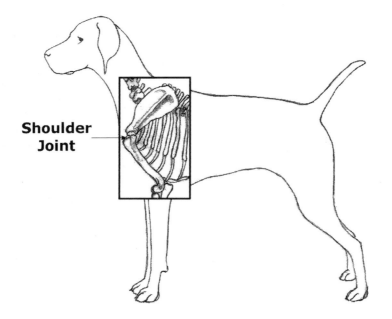

Illustration 5.4. Stabilized Joint: *The Shoulder Joint (The Glenohumeral Joint).*

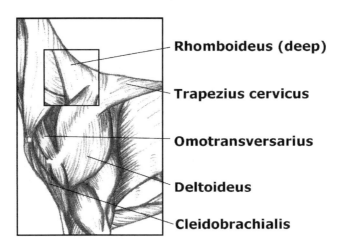

Illustration 5.5. Muscles To Be Stretched: *Rhomboideus, Trapezius cervicus, Omotransversarius, Deltoideus, Cleidobrachialis.*

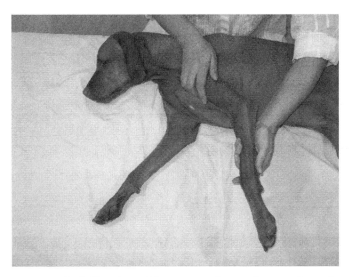

Photo 5.5. Joint Stabilization: *Place your palm on the scapula and wrap the fingers around the cranial aspect of the shoulder joint. Firmly press your palm downward towards the ribs. Hold beneath the elbow with the other hand.*

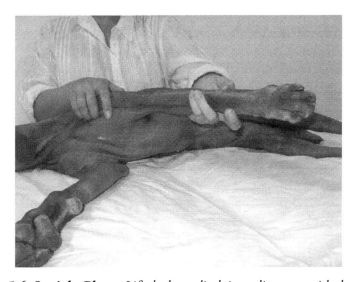

Photo 5.6. Straight Plane: *Lift the lower limb into alignment with the shoulder joint creating a straight plane.*

Attention! If your dog has a diagnosis of shoulder osteochondrosis dissecans (OCD), elbow dysplasia, or any sign of shoulder or elbow pain, DO NOT do this stretch. Consult your veterinarian for stretching recommendations.

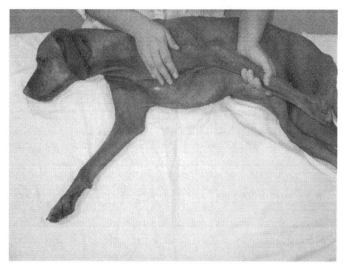

Photo 5.7. Stretch: *Maintaining the straight plane, begin the stretch by reaching the elbow backward allowing it to straighten as the leg moves back. The scapula will naturally rotate beneath the stabilizing hand in the direction of the stretch. Allow this scapular rotation, continuing to press downward towards the ribs. Continue to reach the leg backward until feeling a slight resistance. Hold for 30 seconds.*

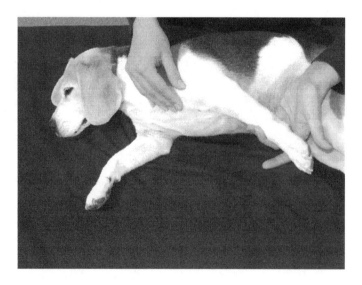

Photo 5.8. Small dog stretch: *For smaller dogs, fingers are adequate to maintain joint stabilization, straight plane, and stretch.*

Shoulder Abduction Stretch

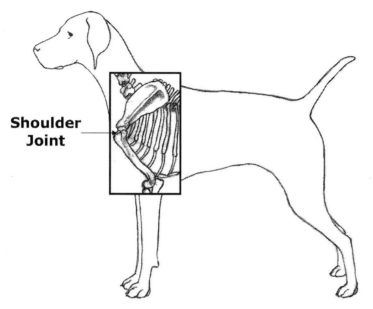

Shoulder Joint

Illustration 5.6 Stabilized Joint: *The Shoulder Joint (The Glenohumeral Joint).*

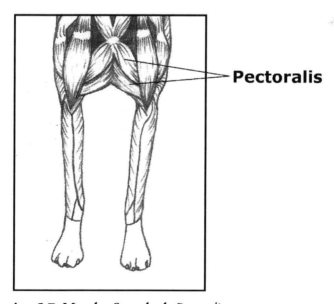

Pectoralis

Illustration 5.7. Muscles Stretched: *Pectoralis.*

The chest muscles are large powerful muscles that originate at the sternum and ribs and attach to the humerus and/or scapula. Contraction of these muscles helps to stabilize the highly mobile scapula and assist with movement of the forelimb. Tight chest muscles are fairly common. One reason might be due the fact that dogs have great difficulty stretching their own chest muscles. Another reason might be that dogs over utilize these muscles in activities such as twisting and turning maneuvers while negotiating tight turns in agility (or squirrel chasing). Because these muscles span the medial aspect of the shoulder joint, it is imperative that a secure stabilization and straight plane movement is maintained throughout the stretch. Without these two critical elements, the medial aspect of the shoulder joint capsule may be stretched instead of the chest muscles.

Attention! Look closely at the photos and note carefully how the stabilizing hand leads the scapula off the rig cage during the stretch. The lifting of the scapula ensures the medial aspect of the shoulder joint capsule is not stretched. If the scapula is not gently guided off the rib cage, then the stretch will not be achieved in the chest muscles and may instead incorrectly stretch the supporting ligaments on the medial aspect of the shoulder joint. Incorrectly performing this stretch predisposes the dog to pain and injury.

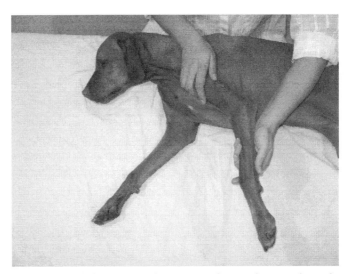

Photo 5.9. Joint Stabilization: *Place your palm on the scapula and wrap your fingers around the cranial aspect of the shoulder joint. Firmly lift the portion of the scapula beneath the fingers off the ribs an inch as you press the portion of the scapula closest to your body (the dorsal border) downwards towards the ribs. The motion is a tilting motion.*

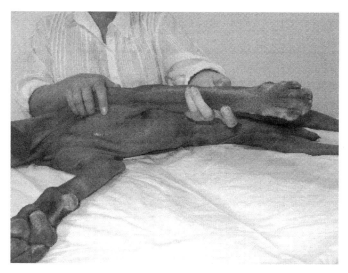

Photo 5.10. Straight Plane: *Lift the distal limb into alignment with the shoulder joint creating a straight plane. Notice how the fingers are holding and lifting the cranial portion of the scapula as the palm continues to stabilize.*

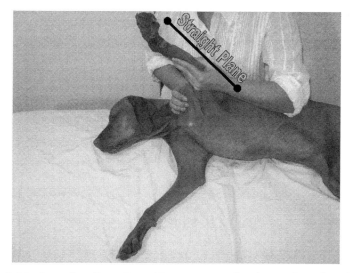

Photo 5.11. Stretch—Bent Leg: *For very muscular dogs or large breeds, allow the elbow to remain bent throughout the stretch. Maintain a straight plane by lifting the forelimb up towards the ceiling as you guide the scapula off the chest with the fingers. Stabilize the dorsal border of the scapula by pressing your palm towards the ribs. You will feel the scapula slide towards you as you lift the limb. Lift until you feel a slight resistance at the cranial aspect of the scapula. Hold for 30 seconds.*

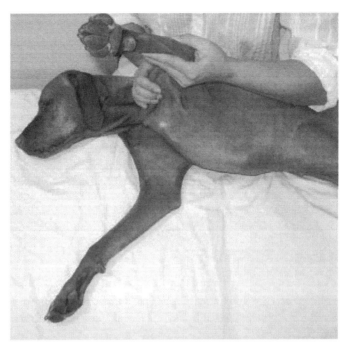

Photo 5.12. Stretch—Straight Leg: *For less muscular dogs and breeds that naturally have more flexibility such as Vizslas, Poodles, and Border Collies, gently straighten the elbow as you lift the leg towards the ceiling using the above instructions. Lift until you feel a slight resistance at the cranial aspect of the scapula. Hold for 30 seconds.*

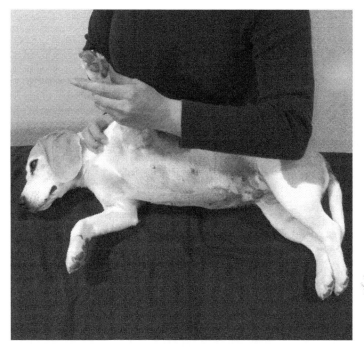

Photo 5.13. Small dog stretch: *For smaller dogs, fingers are adequate to maintain joint stabilization, straight plane, and stretch. You may stretch with a bent or straight elbow. This highly competitive Beagle had fairly tight chest muscles, so I chose the bent leg stretch.*

Shoulder Adduction Stretch

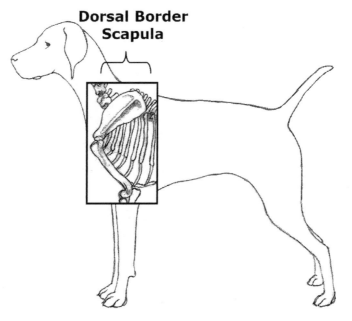

Illustration 5.8. Stabilization: *Movement stabilization on the dorsal border of the scapula.*

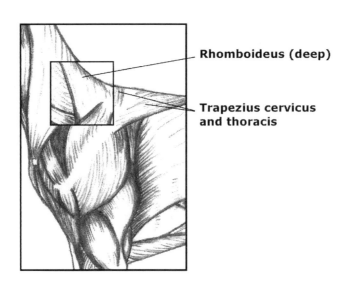

Illustration 5.9. Muscles Stretched: *Trapezius cervicus and thoracis, Rhomboideus.*

The scapula, a flat bone that moves forward, backward, and upward, has muscle attachments to both the ribs and the cervical and thoracic spine. These muscles function in part to coordinate movement of the fore limb. One of the ways it must coordinate movement is by stabilizing the scapula snugly against the rib cage which in turn allows the muscles of the forelimb to move correctly. Any time the dog is not at rest, these scapular muscles are hard at work and can become fatigued and prone to injury from overuse. In order to stretch the muscles of the upper back which assist the scapula with stabilization and movement, we want the scapula to gently glide down the rib cage allowing the muscle fibers to lengthen and stretch.

Attention! If your dog has been diagnosed with elbow dysplasia, osteochondrosis dissecans (OCD) of the shoulder or elbow or shows any signs of pain in the forelimb, this stretch may be harmful or painful. Do not stretch until your dog has been cleared by your veterinarian.

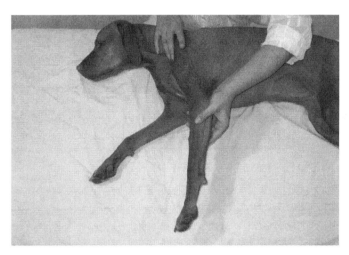

Photo 5.14. Movement Stabilization: *Place the hand over the scapula putting the heel of the hand over the edge of the scapula between the dorsal border of the scapula and the spine. With the other hand firmly grasp just below the elbow joint.*

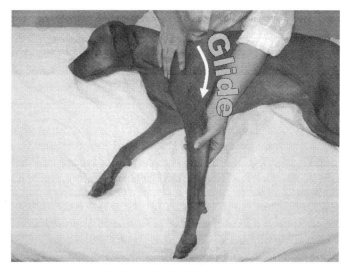

Photo 5.15. Stretch: *With the heel of the hand over the dorsal border of the scapula, begin to glide the scapula down the ribs in the direction of the foot. With the other hand at the elbow, guide the limb downward, away from the body. Allow the feet to relax onto the table. Hold for 30 seconds.*

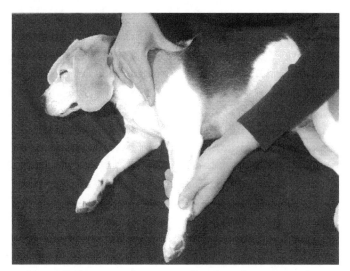

Photo 5.16. Small dog stretch: *For smaller dogs, fingers are adequate to maintain movement stabilization and stretch. There is generally no need to pull on the forelimb—just holding and guiding it is enough.*

Elbow Flexion and Extension Stretch

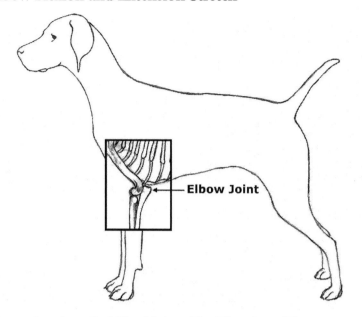

Illustration 5.10. Stabilized Joint: *The Elbow Joint (The Humeroradioulnar Joint).*

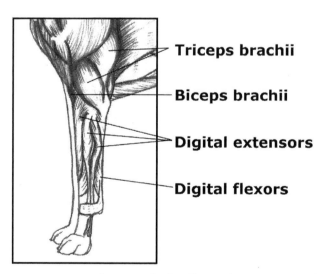

Illustration 5.11. Muscles Stretched: Elbow Flexion: *Triceps brachii, Digital flexors.* **Elbow Extension:** *Biceps brachii, Digital extensors.*

Because of the anatomical arrangement of the bones at the elbow, it functions primarily as a hinge joint that only flexes and extends. Some of the muscles involved in moving the elbow are also involved in moving the shoulder and carpus joints making patterns of tightness fairly common. For example, if the muscles on the cranial aspect of the shoulder joint are tight, the muscles on the cranial aspect of the elbow and carpus may also be tight.

Attention! If your dog has a diagnosis of elbow dysplasia, osteochondrosis dissecans (OCD) of the shoulder or elbow or shows any signs of pain in the forelimb, this stretch may be harmful or painful. Do not stretch until your dog has been cleared by your veterinarian.

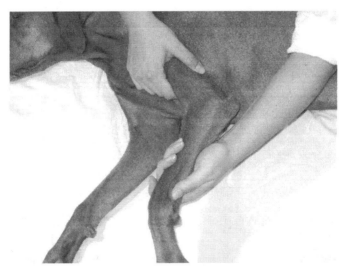

Photo 5.17. Joint Stabilization/Straight Plane: *Grasp the humerus firmly with the stabilizing hand. With the other hand hold the radius and ulna firmly. Do not squeeze tightly with this lower hand as there is some movement between the radius and ulna that needs to be avoided for this stretch. Lift the distal limb into a straight plane with the shoulder.*

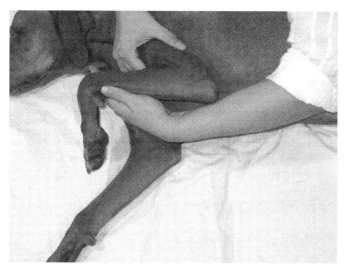

Photo: 5.18. Flexion: *Leave the stabilizing hand where it started. Bend the forearm up towards the nose. Hold for 30 seconds.*

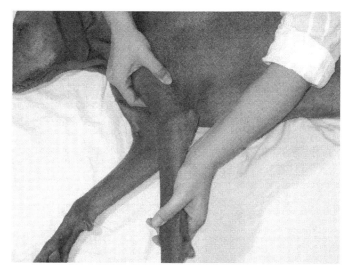

Photo: 5.19. Extension: *Leave the stabilizing hand where it started. Extend the elbow downwards. Because of the anatomical arrangement of the bones, the elbow will not straighten all the way. Hold for 30 seconds.*

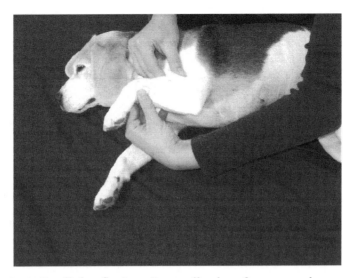

Photo 5.20. Small dog flexion: *For smaller dogs, fingers are adequate to maintain joint stabilization, straight plane, and stretch.*

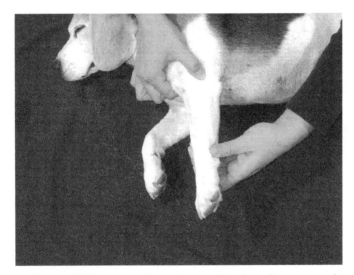

Photo 5.20b. Small dog extension: *For smaller dogs, fingers are adequate to maintain joint stabilization, straight plane, and stretch.*

Carpus Flexion and Extension Stretch

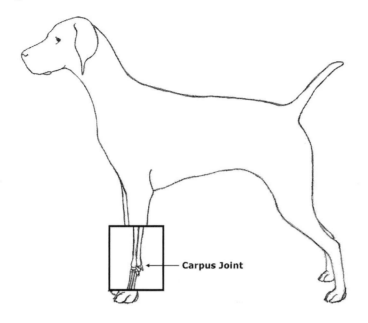

Illustration 5.12. Stabilized Joint: *The Carpus Joint (The Antebrachiocarpal Joint).*

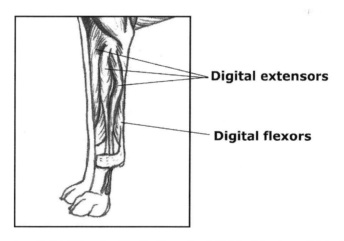

Illustration 5.13. Muscles To Be Stretched: Wrist Flexion: *Digital extensors.* **Wrist Extension:** *Digital flexors.*

The carpus joint is designed to absorb **concussive** forces during movement and to assist with propulsion. In order to do this effectively, the supportive ligaments must be intact in order to provide a high level of stability while still permitting the natural flexibility that makes this joint so important for healthy movement. The muscles that assist with propulsion on the caudal aspect of the joint are very strong and predisposed to overuse injuries. If these caudal muscles which act as flexors of the carpal joint become overly tight, they will prevent effective absorption of the concussive forces on the forelimb. Stretching the muscles on both sides of the carpus joint is an excellent way to assist with injury prevention of this important joint.

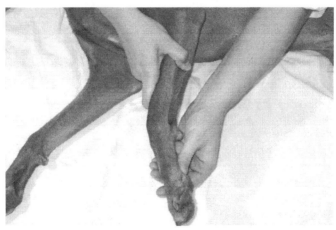

Photo 5.21. Joint Stabilization: *Hold the radius and ulna with your stabilizing hand. Gently grasp the metacarpals below the carpus. Lift the limb into a straight plane.*

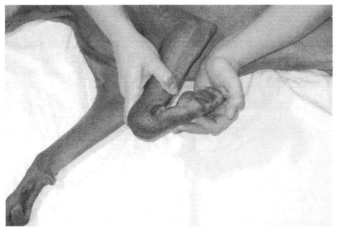

Photo 5.22. Flexion: *Bend the carpus. Hold 30 seconds.*

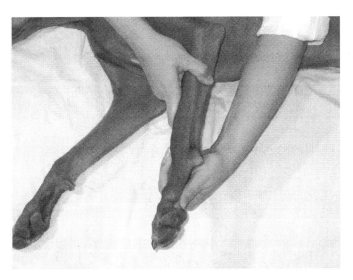

Photo 5.23. Extension: *Straighten the carpus. Hold for 30 seconds.*

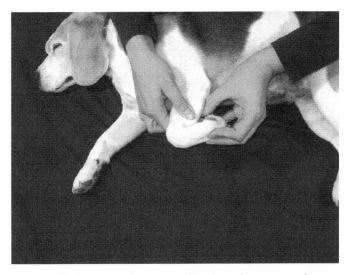

Photo 5.24. Small dog stretch: *For smaller dogs, fingers are adequate to maintain joint stabilization, straight plane, and stretch.*

Foot Flexion and Extension Stretch

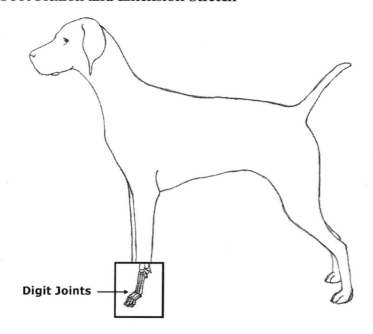

Digit Joints

Illustration 5.14. Stabilized Joint: *The Digit Joints (The Metacarpophalangeal Joints).*

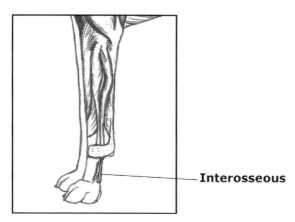

Interosseous

Illustration 5.15. Muscles To Be Stretched: *Interosseous.*

The joints of the feet, the metacarpophalangeal joints and the phalangeal joints, are similar to the carpal joint in that they provide a high level of stability by virtue of their supportive ligaments, while allowing for a high level of flexibility which is required for healthy and accurate movement. The feet also provide an additional vital function to the movement of the dog—the nerves in the feet tell the dog about the position and movement of its limbs in space. This sensory response, knows as **proprioception**, is vitally important for balance, movement, and navigating uneven terrain. Stretching the feet is an important way to ensure the muscles and nerves of the feet remain healthy.

Attention! Many dogs are touch sensitive on their feet. Please refer to the section on Contact Comfort Section in Chapter 3, page 44-46, to assist your dog with making this important stretch as comfortable as possible.

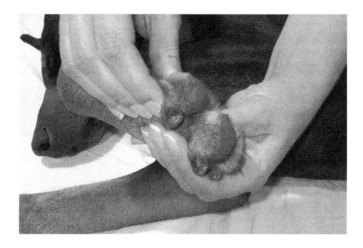

Photo 5.25. Joint Stabilization: *Hold two adjacent phalanges above the toe pads.*

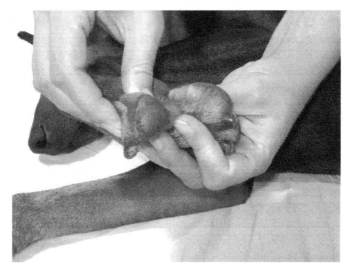

Photo 5.26. Stretch. *Gently wiggle these bones back and forth a few times, then hold the stretch for 30 seconds. Switch to the toes next door and wiggle again. Remember the back feet as well.*

Chapter 6
HIND LIMB STRETCHES

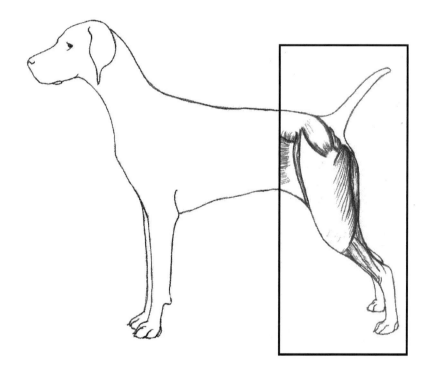

Illustration 6.1. Hind Limb

The hind limb creates power for forward movement and jumping. This power comes from the anatomical arrangement of the joints and the large muscles of the low back, hip, and thigh. This anatomical arrangement is also the reason why straight plane movement is critically important in the hind limb. Incorrect alignment of the joints can place damaging forces through the connective tissues that support the hip and stifle. In addition, the prevalence of hip dysplasia, patellar luxation, and cruciate ligament injuries require that particular attention be given to straight plane movement to ensure the safety and efficacy of the stretches.

Attention! Due to the fact that many low back, hip, and stifle injuries are silent or subclinical (the dog does not have overt signs of pain or injury), it is imperative all dogs must be evaluated by their veterinarian before beginning any hind limb stretches.

The Hip

The hip is a ball and socket joint that moves through a rotational range of motion. Because the hip is very mobile, it requires a strong and comfortable stabilizing force. Please be aware that dogs with arthritis or hip dysplasia may find the stabilizing pressure uncomfortable. If this is the case with your dog, ask your veterinarian for stabilization alternatives.

Attention! Hip dysplasia is a debilitating degeneration of the hip joint that ranges from painful movement to risk of subluxation of the hip joint. If your dog shows signs of pain in the hind limb, please see your veterinarian for stretch recommendations.

Hip Extension Stretch

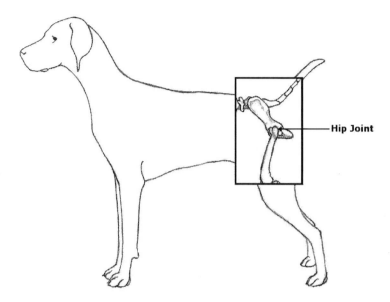

Illustration 6.2. Stabilized Joint: *The Hip Joint (The Coxofemoral Joint).*

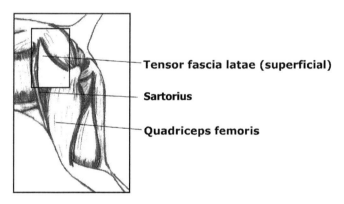

Illustration 6.3. Muscles To Be Stretched: *Quadriceps femoris, Sartorius, Tensor fascia latae.*

Attention! Please refrain from stretching the cranial hip in breeds that are prone to patellar luxation: toy breeds and giant breeds until cleared by your veterinarian. If your dog has hip dysplasia or exhibits pain in the low back or hind limb, please consult your veterinarian for stretch recommendations.

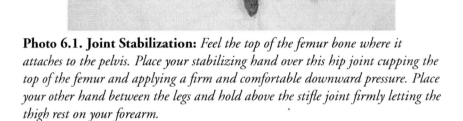

Photo 6.1. Joint Stabilization: *Feel the top of the femur bone where it attaches to the pelvis. Place your stabilizing hand over this hip joint cupping the top of the femur and applying a firm and comfortable downward pressure. Place your other hand between the legs and hold above the stifle joint firmly letting the thigh rest on your forearm.*

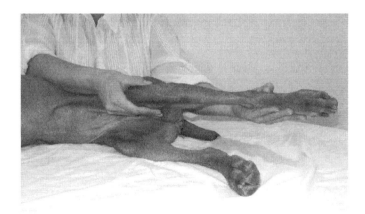

Photo 6.2. Straight Plane: *Create a straight plane by lifting the distal hind limb into alignment with the hip joint.*

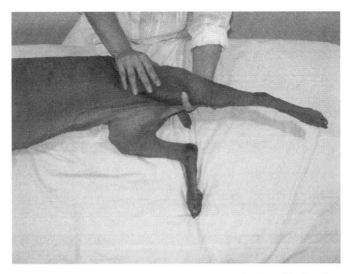

Photo 6.3. Stretch: *Continue to press down towards the table firmly with your stabilizing hand as you extend the leg back towards the tail. The stifle will naturally extend. Stretch until you feel a slight resistance. Hold for 30 seconds.*

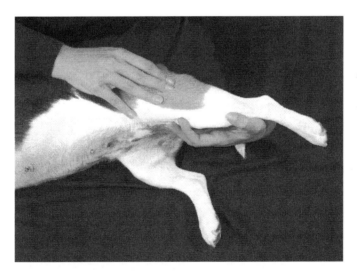

Photo 6.4. Small dog stretch: *For smaller dogs, fingers are adequate to maintain joint stabilization, straight plane, and stretch.*

Hip Flexion Stretch

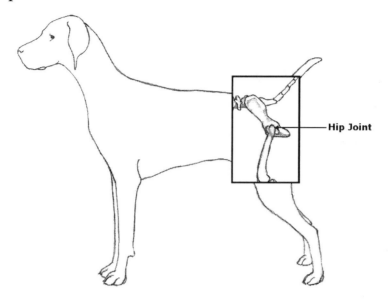

Illustration 6.4. Stabilized Joint: *The Hip Joint (The Coxofemoral Joint).*

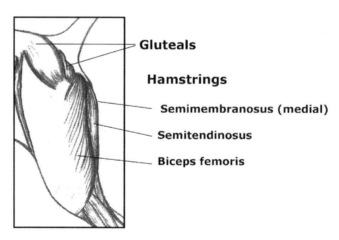

Illustration 6.5. Muscles To Be Stretched: Bent Leg Stretch: *Gluteal Muscle Group.* **Straight Leg Stretch:** *The Hamstrings Muscle Group (Semimembranosus, Semitendinosus, Biceps Femoris).*

Attention! Please refrain from stretching the hip if your dog has hip dysplsia or exhibits pain in the low back or hind limb, consult your veterinarian for stretch recommendations.

A Stretch Question

Q: Why stretch both with a bent leg and a straight leg?

A: The bent leg stretches the Gluteal Muscle Group; the straight leg stretches the Hamstring Muscle Group.

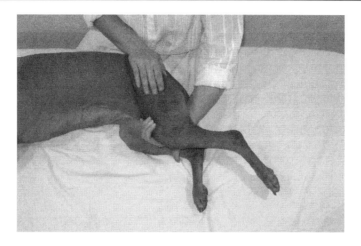

Photo 6.5. Joint Stabilization: *Feel the top of the femur bone where it attaches to the pelvis. Place your stabilizing hand over this hip joint cupping the top of the femur and applying a firm and comfortable downward pressure. Place your other hand between the legs and hold above the stifle joint firmly letting the thigh rest on your forearm.*

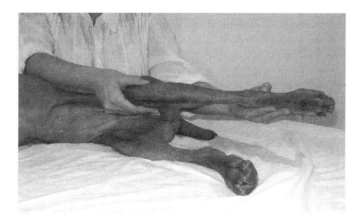

Photo 6.6. Straight Plane: *Create a straight plane by lifting the distal hind limb into alignment with the hip joint.*

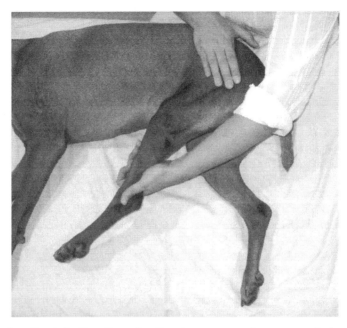

Photo 6.7. Straight Leg Stretch: *Continue to press down towards the table firmly with your stabilizing hand as you straighten the leg forward guiding the stifle to straighten. Stretch until you feel a slight resistance. Hold for 30 seconds.*

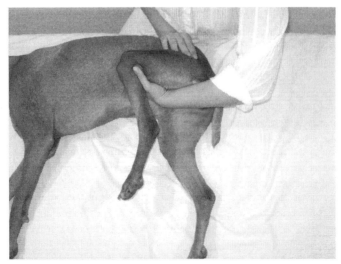

Photo 6.8. Bent Leg Stretch: *Continue to press down towards the table firmly with your stabilizing hand as you bring the stifle forward against the lateral stomach. Stretch until you feel a slight resistance. Hold for 30 seconds.*

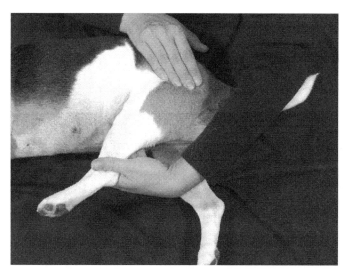

Photo 6.9. Small Dog Straight Leg Stretch: *For smaller dogs, use your fingers to maintain straight plane, joint stabilization, and stretch while allowing the stifle to straighten.*

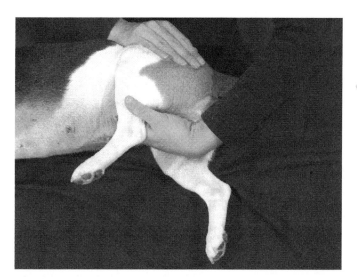

Photo 6.10. Small Dog Bent Leg Stretch: *For smaller dogs, use your fingers to maintain straight plane, joint stabilization, and stretch while allowing the stifle to bend.*

Hip Abduction Stretch

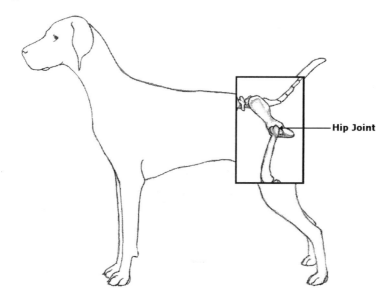

Illustration 6.6. Stabilized Joint: *The Hip Joint (The Coxofemoral Joint).*

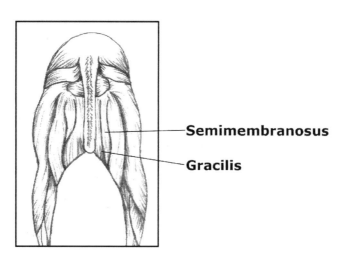

Illustration 6.7. Muscles To Be Stretched: *Gracilis, Semimembranosus.*
Deep muscles not seen: Pectineus and Adductor.

Please refrain from stretching the medial hip if your dog has hip dysplsia or exhibits pain in the low back or stifle, consult your veterinarian for stretch recommendations.

Attention!

In order to stretch the inner thigh muscles, you must maintain a straight plane throughout the length of the hind limb just as you do in a chest stretch. Imagine you have the dog's leg resting on a board. If you allow the hind limb to turn in any direction you will no longer be stretching the hip adductors and you may be putting additional stresses on the medial ligaments of the stifle joint (some of the muscles that cross the medial hip also cross the medial stifle, so stretching one will stretch the other).

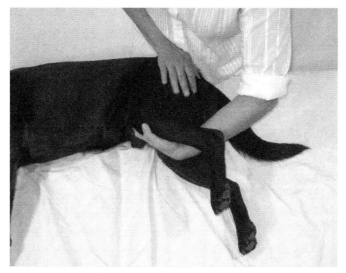

Photo 6.11. Joint Stabilization: *Feel the top of the femur bone where it attaches to the pelvis. Place your stabilizing hand over this hip joint cupping the top of the femur and applying a firm and comfortable downward pressure. Place your other hand between the legs and hold above the stifle joint firmly letting the thigh rest on your forearm.*

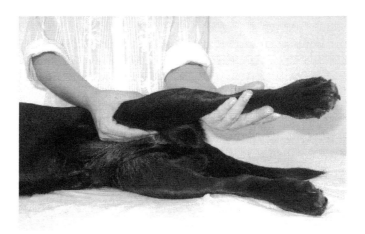

Photo 6.12. Straight Plane: *Create a straight plane by lifting the distal hind limb into alignment with the hip joint.*

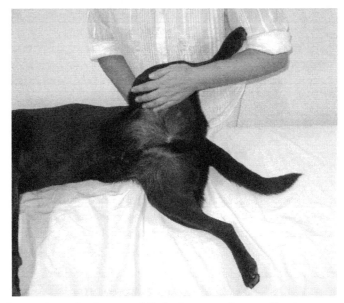

Photo 6.13a. Stretch: *Begin to lift the leg towards you, allowing your stabilizing hand to tip towards you as the leg lifts. Hold for 30 seconds.*

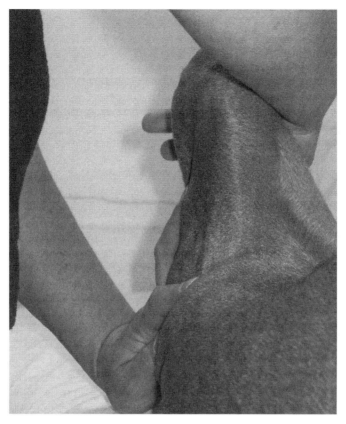

Photo 6.13b. Stretch: *Allow your stabilizing hand to tip towards you as the leg lifts.*

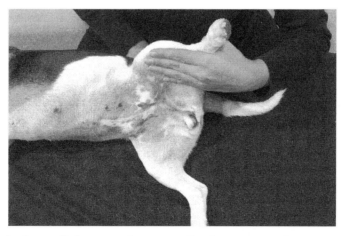

Photo 6.14. Small dog stretch: *For smaller dogs, use your fingers to maintain straight plane, joint stabilization, and stretch.*

Hip Adduction Stretches

Please see "Back Rotation" page 130 for stretches of the lateral hip.

Stifle

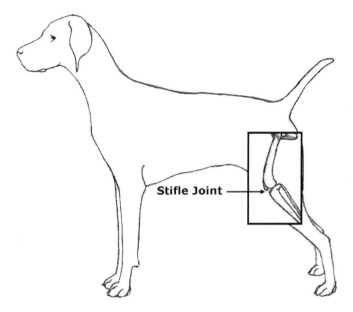

Illustration 6.8. Stabilized Joint: *The Stifle Joint (The Femorotibial Joint and the Femoropatellar Joint).*

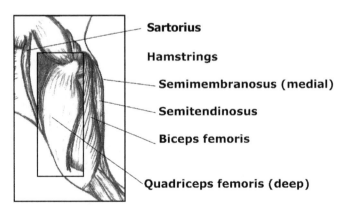

Illustration 6.9. Muscles Stretched: Flexion: *Quadriceps femoris, Sartorius.* **Extension:** *Hamstrings Muscle Group (Semimembranosus, Semitendinosus, Biceps Femoris).*

The stifle joint is a complicated hinge joint that allows for flexion and extension of the stifle. The "complication" comes from the anatomical arrangement of the patella, or knee cap, on the cranial aspect of the hinge portion of the joint. The patella provides a critically important mechanical advantage to the movement of the stifle joint—if the patella wasn't present, the stifle would not be able to straighten into full extension. Part of the hind leg's ability to create power comes from the stifle joint's ability to flex and then quickly extend during running and jumping activities. Maintaining the integrity of the stifle and its supporting structures is of critical importance for the safety and proper function of the joint.

Also of critical importance is ensuring and maintaining the integrity of the cruciate ligaments. These ligaments hold the femur and tibia together allowing for proper movement of the joint. Some dogs have "silent" or subclinical strains, sprains, or even tears in the cruciate ligaments. Injury to the cruciate ligaments causes instability of the stifle joint. **Stretching an unstable stifle joint MAY cause permanent injury to your dog.** Only a veterinarian can correctly diagnose a cruciate ligament injury. To reiterate: have your dog evaluated by your veterinarian prior to proceeding with any stifle stretches.

Safety Issue! To ensure proper forces through the patella during the cranial stifle stretch, the femur bone should be at about a 90 degree angle with the back. *Do not* hold the femur back and then stretch the stifle! You can injure the stifle joint.

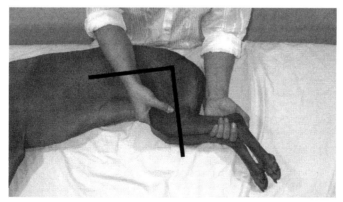

Photo 6.15a. Correct Starting Position: *The femur should be at about a 90 degree angle with the back to ensure patellar safety while stretching the cranial stifle.*

97

All dogs must be evaluated and cleared by their veterinarian prior to doing any stifle stretches. It is critically important that your veterinarian assesses the stability of the stifle before stretching.

Attention!

Photos 6.15b. Incorrect Starting Position: *Do not stretch the stifle with the femur extended back. It puts additional stress through the cranial stifle joint putting the patella at risk for luxation and cranial cruciate at risk for tears.*

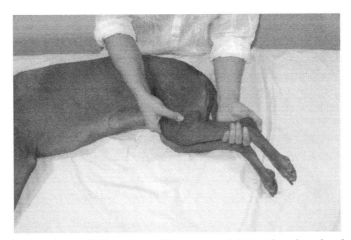

Photo 6.16. Joint Stabilization: *Place your stabilizing hand under the leg about half way up the femur to prevent pressures on the tendons attached to the patella. Place your other hand beneath the leg below the stifle. Move the femur bone into a 90 degree angle with the back.*

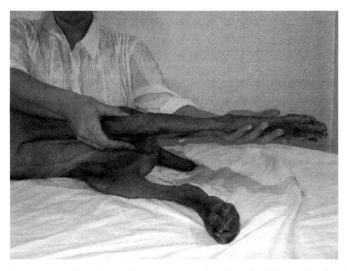

Photo 6.17. Straight Plane: *Create a straight plane by lifting the distal hind limb into alignment with the hip joint.*

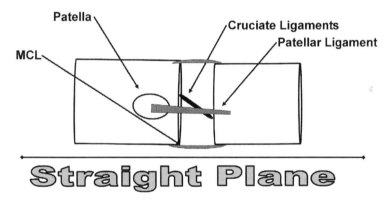

Illustration 2.13. Correct Alignment of the Stifle Joint: *When the stifle joint is held in a straight plane during a stretch, the patella, patellar ligament, cruciate ligaments, and medial collateral ligament are in correct alignment. There is no risk for injury.*

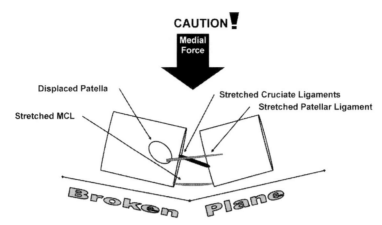

Illustration 2.14. Medial Force, Incorrect Alignment of the Stifle Joint:
When the stifle joint is held in a broken plane during a stretch, the patella, patellar ligament, cruciate ligaments, and medial collateral ligament are stretched out of correct alignment. This puts the patella at risk for luxation and the cruciates at risk for tears.

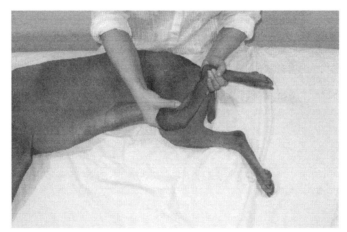

Photo 6.18. Flexion: *Maintain a straight plane throughout the stretch. Leave your stabilizing hand on the femur in the starting position. Bend the knee bringing the hock up towards the point of the hip until you feel a slight resistance. Hold for 30 seconds.*

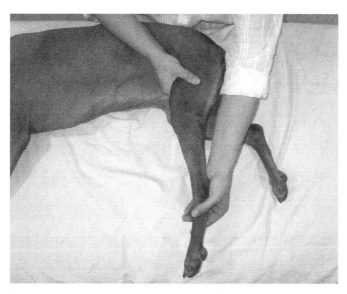

Photo 6.19. Extension: *Maintain a straight plane throughout the stretch. Leave your stabilizing hand on the femur in the starting position. Straighten the stifle downward until you feel a slight resistance. Hold for 30 seconds.*

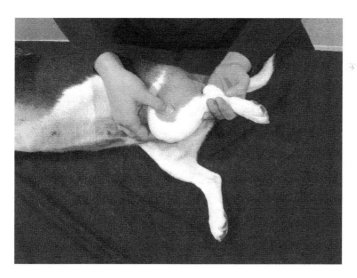

Photo 6.20. Small dog flexion stretch: *For smaller dogs, use your fingers to maintain a straight plane, joint stabilization, and stretch while allowing the stifle to flex (bend).*

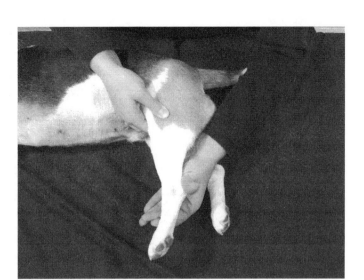

Photo 6.21. Small dog extension stretch: *For smaller dogs, use your fingers to maintain a straight plane, joint stabilization, and stretch while allowing the stifle to extend (straighten).*

A Stretch Question

Q: Why is it recommended that I not stretch any of the hip muscles if my dog is prone to hip dysplasia but, only the cranial hip and stifle if my dog is prone to patellar luxation?

A: Hip dysplasia involves a risk of hip subluxation, especially if the disease is advanced. Because the hip is a ball and socket joint, *the hip can subluxate in any direction.* The stifle joint, on the other hand, is a hinge joint, it only flexes and extends. Because the patella is located on the cranial aspect of the stifle, the *stretching direction that can cause patellar luxation is stifle flexion.* Flexion is also the direction that can cause cruciate ligament injury.

Hock Stretch

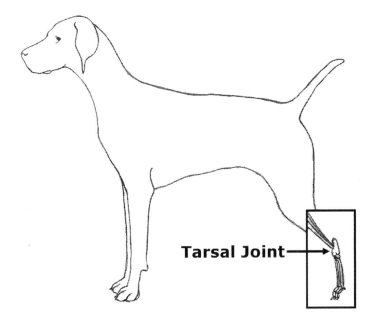

Illustration 6.10. Stabilized Joint: *The Tarsal Joint (The Tibiotarsal Joint).*

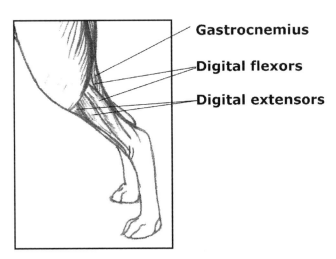

Illustration 6.11. Muscles Stretched: Flexion: *Gastrocnemius, Digital Flexors.* **Extension:** *Digital Extensors.*

The hock, or tarsal joint, is the joint between the tibia and the bones of the foot. The arrangement of the bones of the tarsus and the muscles that surround it are designed to absorb concussive forces during movement. The bones and the muscles in this area are long and lean. Although it is difficult to feel the muscles of the hock because they are so long and lean, it is quite easy to feel the resistance of the muscles when stretching, especially when flexing the hock. These muscles are the dog's "calf" muscles, that attach to the heel bone as the calcanean tendon (achille's tendon). If your dog runs—short distances or long—he will most likely have tightness in these muscles. When stretching the hock in the opposite direction, extending the joint, the calcaneus (heel bone) actually hits the tibia. This is why the hock doesn't straighten all the way—it can't.

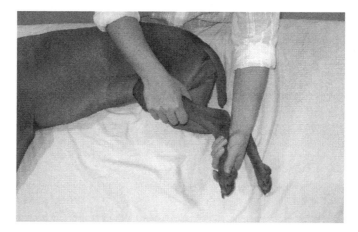

Photo 6.22. Joint Stabilization: *Hold the tibia firmly with your stabilizing hand. Encircle the metatarsals with the other hand. Lift the leg into a straight plane.*

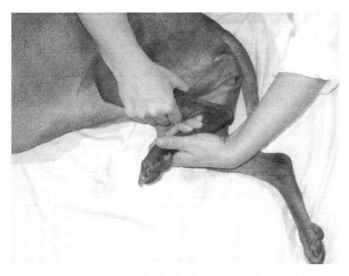

Photo 6.23. Flexion: *Flex (bend) the hock until you feel a slight resistance. Hold for 30 seconds.*

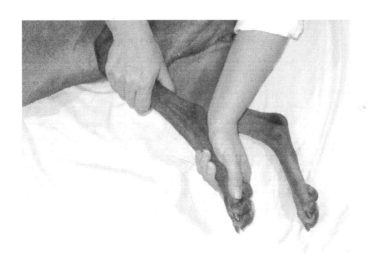

Photo 6.24. Extension: *Extend (straighten) the hock. It will not go completely straight! It's not supposed to. Hold for 30 seconds.*

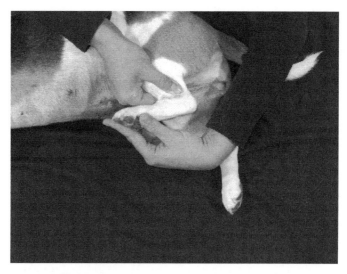

Photo 6.25. Small dog flexion: *For smaller dogs, you will use your fingers to maintain straight plan, joint stabilization, and stretch.*

Photo 6.25b. Small dog extension: *For smaller dogs, you will use your fingers to maintain straight plan, joint stabilization, and stretch.*

Chapter 7
NECK AND BACK
STRETCHES

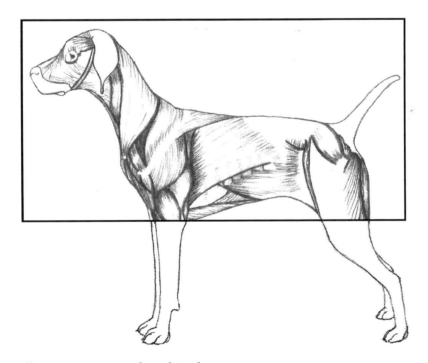

Illustration 7.1. Neck and Back

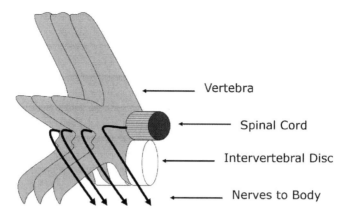

Illustration 7.2. Vertebra with nerves.

The spine is composed of bony vertebrae and fibrous intervertebral discs that run from the base of the skull to the tail. The boney spine's primary purpose is to protect the spinal cord. Combined with the intervertebral disks, the boney spine is capable of a myriad of movement combinations (i.e., flexion, extension, axial rotation) as well as transferring the power generated by the rear limbs to the forelimb.

The spine also maintains the anatomical relationship between the spinal cord and the spinal nerves. The spinal nerves send all the messages about movement to and from the muscles and the spinal cord. Some of these messages are then sent to the brain for further processing. Some of them remain within the spinal cord. It is also important to note that all the information about the organs in the body (heart, lungs, gastrointestinal tract, kidney, liver, etc.) is sent to and from the brain via the spinal nerves. Appropriately, stretching the spine may not only improve movement, but improve organ function as well.

Dogs naturally stretch their spines on a regular basis. However, if your dog is very active or is aging, the muscles along the spine can tighten and the facet joints that connect the vertebrae together can tighten up as well predisposing the dog to injuries, arthritis, and/or pain.

Stretching the spine will feel much different than stretching the limbs and it requires a different technique as well. The joints that connect the vertebrae to each other vary in purpose depending on where you are in the spine. The joints in the upper neck allow for a large range of movement—your dog can look up (extend), look down (flex), and rotate his neck as needed for daily activities. The joints in the thoracic region are limited in their movement due to their attachments to the ribs. The joints in the lumbar region can extend, flex, and minimally axially rotate at the lumbosacral joint.

The nerves that control critical body functions such as respiration and balance run through the spine. The majority of them are between the back of the skull and the first two cervical vertebrae. Diaphragm function is controlled via the spinal nerves in the lower cervical vertebra. The diaphragm not only assists in respiration but in heart function as well. Other organ systems are controlled by other areas of the spine.

Attention! Atlantoaxial subluxation occurs when the second cervical vertebra (C2) is displaced from the first cervical vertebra (C1). C2 slips into the spinal cord causing neurological damage that may include paralysis. It is most commonly seen in young toy and miniature breeds but can be seen in other breeds as well. Other pathologies including cervical spondylomyelopathy, intervertebral disc disease, or nerve injuries can cause permanent injury to your dog far beyond orthopedic problems. To ensure the stability of the spine and to rule out potential spinal issues, have your dog evaluated and cleared by your veterinarian before beginning spine stretches.

The Neck

The neck is the most flexible portion of the spine composed of vertebrae, muscles, and nerves that connect the head to the body. Dogs move their necks frequently to navigate through the world. Decreased flexibility can limit an obedience or agility dog's ability to look up towards its owner, throw off a show dog's top line, or cause pain and discomfort in an older dog. Stretching the muscles of the neck can maintain or increase flexibility to allow for full range of motion.

There are many mobile joints in the neck. Intervertebral facet joints connect one vertebra to next and the cushion-like disks that lie between each vertebra. However, there is only one joint that needs to be stabilized, the Atlanto-occipital joint. This joint is the highly mobile joint that connects the first cervical vertebra to the skull. This joint is so flexible it requires strong manual stabilization to help the dog feel relaxed and to ensure the receptors in and around the joint remain turned off. The high level of flexibility of the neck also means we do not provide a straight plane. When we stretch the neck, it is beneficial for the muscles and joints to rotate as we move through the stretch.

By stretching the neck, we are asking the dog to surrender control of his head, to our hands. This can be very difficult, even for the calmest dog. If you find these neck stretches to be difficult, practice increasing the stabilization by holding the base of the skull gently and firmly, similar to how you would hold an infants head. The rest of the hand can firmly cup the neck—it is this stabilization force over the Atlanto-occipital joint that allows the dog to relax into these stretches.

A Stretch Question

Q: Can I hurt my dog when stretching his neck?

A: Yes you can! You must follow the instructions and listen to your dog. The force your dog puts through his neck during play and fun is much greater than the forces you will put through his neck when stretching. However, if you are stretching incorrectly, your dog will tell you. The most difficult element of these stretches is teaching the dog to relax. Once he does, the stretches will be easy and comfortable for both of you. If you find your dog won't relax it may be a sign something is wrong. Please have your dog checked by a veterinarian.

Neck Flexion Stretch

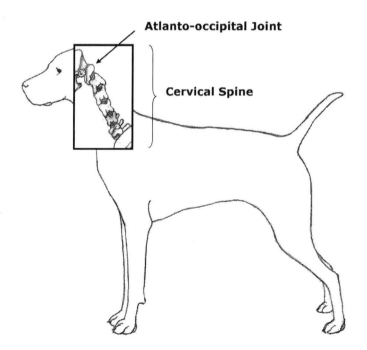

Illustration 7.3. Stabilized Joint: *The Atlanto-occipital Joint.*

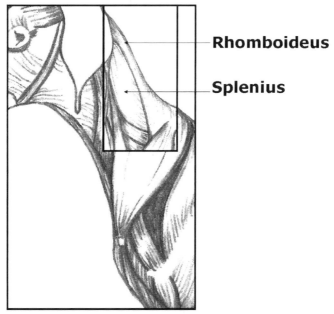

Illustration 7.4. Muscles To Be Stretched: *Rhomboideus cervicus. Deep muscles not seen: Semispinalis capitus, and nuchal ligament.*

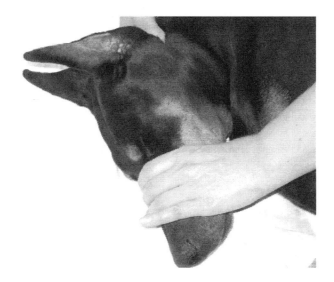

Photo 7.1. Stabilization: *With your stabilizing hand, open your thumb and pointer finger wide and cup the base of the skull gently and firmly. Place your other hand high on the top of the nose.*

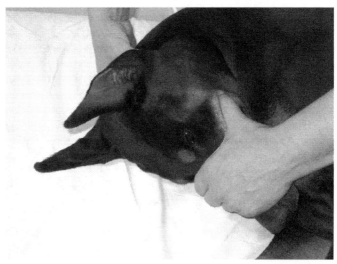

Photo 7.2. Stretch: *With your stabilizing hand, gently guide the upper neck into a flexed position as you tuck the chin towards the chest with your other hand. Hold for 30 seconds.*

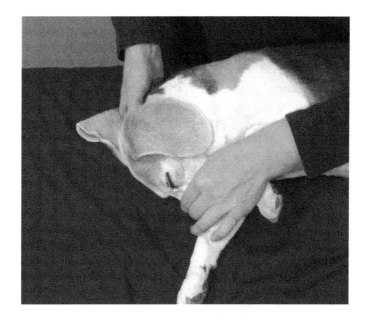

Photo 7.3. Small Dog Stretch: *For smaller dogs you will use your fingers for joint stabilization and stretch.*

Neck Extension Stretch

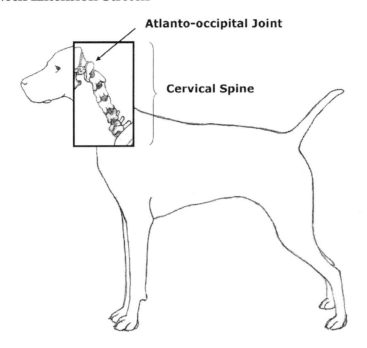

Illustration 7.5. Stabilized Joint: *Atlanto-occipital Joint.*

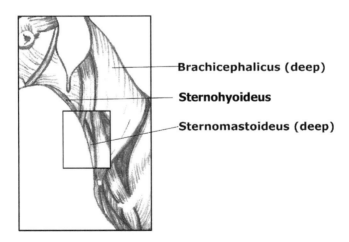

Illustration 7.6. Muscles Stretched: *Sternomastoideus, Sternohyoideus, Brachicephalicus. Deep muscles not seen: Scalenes.*

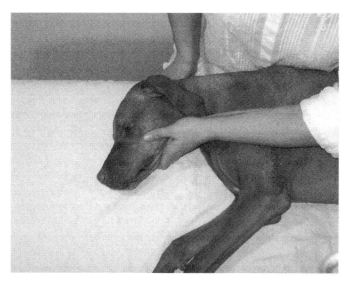

Photo 7.4. Stabilization: *With your stabilizing hand, open your thumb and pointer finger wide and cup the base of the skull firmly. With the other hand cup the mandible from beneath.*

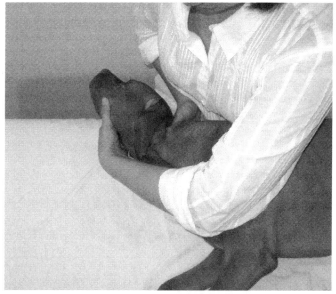

Photo 7.5. Stretch: *With your stabilizing hand, gently guide the upper neck into an extended position as you lift the chin with the other hand. Continue to lift until you feel a slight resistance. Hold for 30 seconds.*

Photo 7.6. Different dogs have different levels of flexibility: *Notice the difference in range of motion between Photo 7.5 and Photo 7.6. Most dogs will have a range similar to the Doberman.*

Photo 7.7. Small dog stretch: *For smaller dogs you will use your fingers for joint stabilization and stretch.*

Neck Rotation Stretch

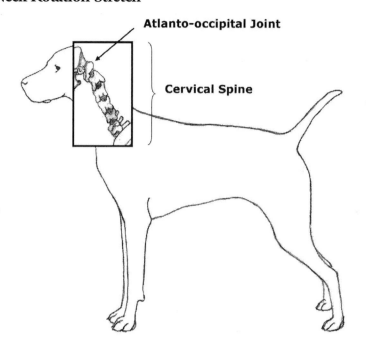

Illustration 7.7. Stabilized Joint: *The Atlanto-occipital Joint.*

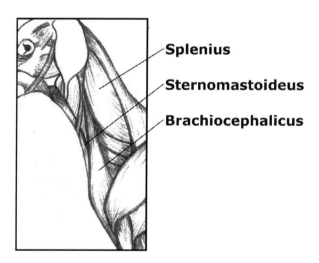

Illustration 7.8. Muscles To Be Stretched: *Sternomastoideus, Splenius, Brachiocephalicus. Deep muscles not seen: Rhomboids.*

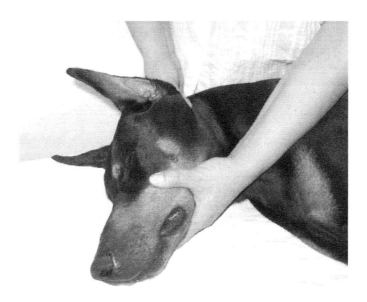

Photo 7.8. Stabilization: *With your stabilizing hand, open the thumb and pointer finger wide and cup the base of the skull firmly. With the other hand, cup the the mandible from beneath.*

Photo 7.9. Stretch: *With your stabilizing hand, gently guide the upper neck into a rotated position while turning the chin up towards the ceiling. Continue to rotate until you feel a slight resistance. Hold for 30 seconds.*

117

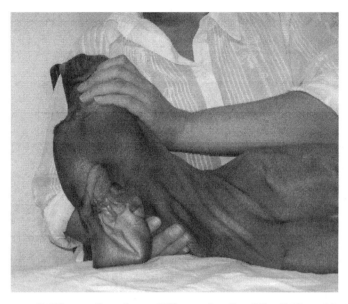

Photo 7.10. Different dogs have different levels of flexibility: *Notice the difference in range of motion between Photo 7.9 and Photo 7.10. The Vizsla shown here is an example of dog with extreme flexibility. Even in this position I did not feel any resistance, I simply stopped the stretch because she clearly has enough flexibility.*

Photo 7.11. Small dog stretch: *For smaller dogs, you will use your fingers for joint stabilization and stretch.*

Neck Side Bending Stretch

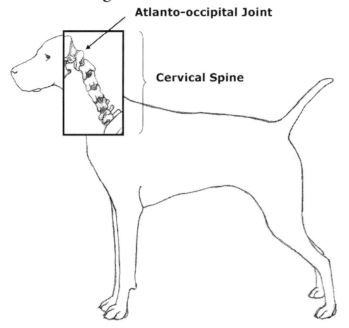

Illustration 7.9. Stabilized Joint: *The Atlanto-occipital Joint.*

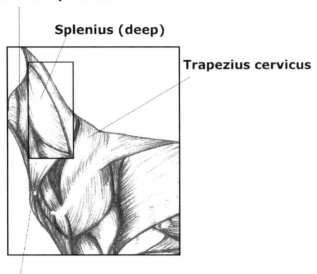

Illustration 7.10. Muscles Stretched: *Trapezius cervicus, Splenius, Brachiocephalicus, Sternocephalicus. Deep muscles not seen: Scalenes, Rhomboids.*

Photo 7.12. Stabilization: *With your stabilizing hand, open your thumb and pointer finger wide and cup the base of the skull firmly. With the other hand, cup the mandible from beneath.*

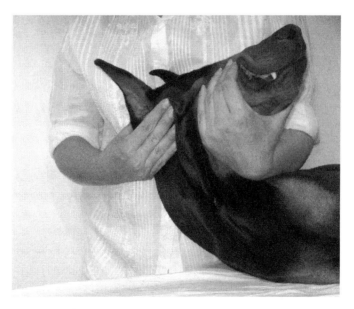

Photo 7.13. Stretch: *With your stabilizing hand gently guide the neck into a side bend as you lift the head towards the ceiling allowing the neck to lift from the table. Continue to lift until you feel a slight resistance. Hold for 30 seconds.*

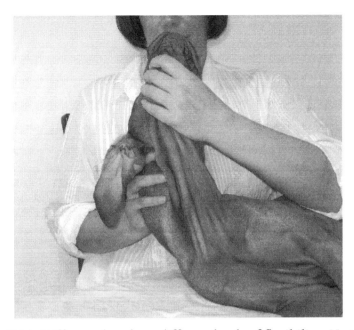

Photo 7.14. Different dogs have different levels of flexibility: *Notice the difference in range of motion between Photo 7.13 and Photo 7.14. Most dogs will have a range similar to the Doberman. The Vizsla shown above is an example of dog with extreme flexibility.*

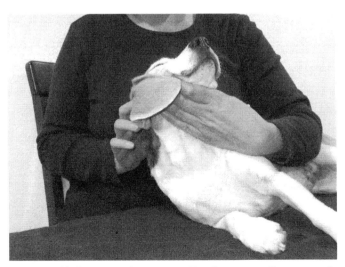

Photo 7.15. Small dog stretch: *For smaller dogs you will use your fingers for joint stabilization and stretch.*

The Back

The back consists of three different segments of the spine: the thoracic region, the portion that is connected to the ribs; the lumbar region, the portion between the ribs and the pelvis; and the sacrum which connects the spine to the pelvis. Long, very strong, muscles run the length of the back from the skull to the pelvis. Beneath these muscles are smaller intervertebral muscles that connect one vertebra to another. Both of these muscles benefit from stretching to maintain muscle length and joint integrity. Tightness of the back muscles can decrease an agility dog's jumping height; throw off the top line of show dogs, or cause pain and discomfort in older dogs. Stretching the muscles of the back can maintain or increase flexibility to allow for a full range of motion.

The back is very mobile so there is no need for straight plane movement. Lateral bending as you flex or extend is a natural part of motion in the back and will not change the muscles you are stretching or the quality of the stretch. Unlike every other stretch in this manual, the spine stretches are the only ones that don't require straight plane movement.

In general, we stabilize the most mobile joint in the area. Because the mobility of the joints in the back are about equal to each other*, there is no highly mobile segment (unless there is an underlying dysfunction) that requires stabilization to keep the receptors turned off and the dog comfortable. Instead, stabilization simply means holding securely to the recommended boney structures.

Attention! The nerves that control movement to the body run through the spinal cord. Underlying problems such as intervertebral disc disease can be exacerbated when stretching your dog. Other diagnoses such as arthritis and lumbosacral instability can cause pain and/or injury. To rule out these or other spine problems, have your dog evaluated by your veterinarian before beginning back stretches.

---

*For the purposes of this book, particularly for stabilization, spine segment movement is considered approximately equal. In clinical terms the junctions between segments—the cervical thoracic, thoracic-lumbar, and lumbosacral, are more mobile than other spine segments.

Back Flexion—Large Dog

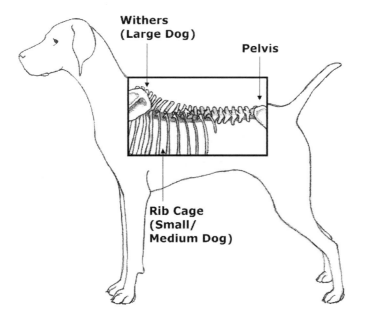

Illustration 7.11. Stabilization: *Pelvic Bone (all dog sizes) and the Withers (large and giant breeds) or the Rib Cage (medium and small breeds).*

Multifidi thoracis and lumborum (very deep)
These muscles are not shown in the illustration—found beneath Longissimus dorsi

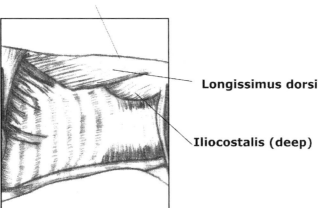

Illustration 7.12. Muscles Stretched: *Longissimus dorsi, Iliocostalis (long muscles of the back), Multifidi thoracis, and Multifidi lumborum (small muscles between vertebrae).*

Attention! Please refrain from stretching dogs with spinal arthritis (diskospondylosis) degenerative disc disease, lumbosacral instability, or any back pain. Consult your veterinarian for stretch recommendations.

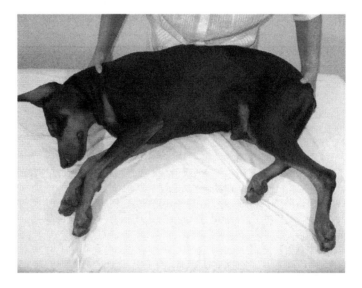

Photo 7.16. Stabilization: *Place one hand at the base of the neck and the other hand on the pelvis. Hold securely.*

Photo 7.17. Stretch: *Firmly pull your hands towards each other. Hold for 30 seconds.*

Back Flexion—Medium to Small Dog

The Doberman on page 120 is a very muscular, medium to large dog who requires increased force to stretch his spine. This much force is not recommended for more flexible breeds such as Poodles or Vizsla, nor is it recommended for small dogs. For these breeds the recommended hand placement is on the more secure ribs instead of the base of the neck. It is important to be aware that just like humans, dogs have floating ribs. The best hand placement is about in the middle of the rib cage where the joints are very stable and secure.

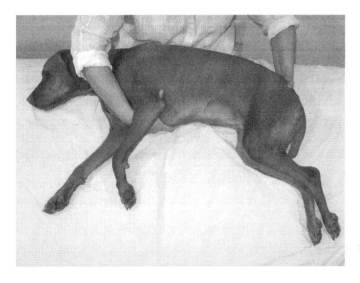

Photo 7.18. Stabilization: *Place one hand in the middle of the rib cage and the other hand on the pelvis. Hold securely.*

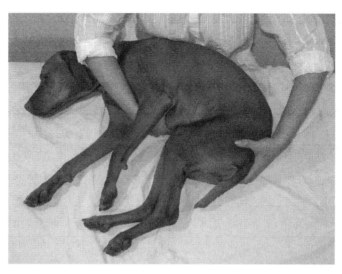

Photo 7.19. Stretch: *Maintain the secure hold on the rib cage as you pull the pelvis in towards the ribs. Hold for 30 seconds.*

A Stretch Question

Q: If a dog can curl up in a tight ball when he is sleeping why can't his back bend that much during this stretch?

A: When the dog is laying flat on his side, it aligns the muscles in a way that will make any tightness more noticeable. When a dog curls up in a ball to sleep, they may be compensating for their tightness by laterally bending their spine. Lateral bending decreases the stretch on the long muscles of the back and makes them look like they have more flexion than they actually do.

Back Extension

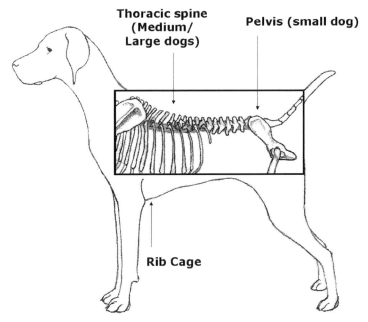

Illustration 7.13. Stabilization: *Rib Cage and Pelvis.*

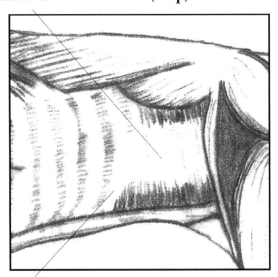

Illustration 7.14. Muscles To Be Stretched: *Rectus Abdominus, Transversus Abdominus. Muscles not seen: External Abdominal Obliques.*

Attention! Degenerative disc disease and arthritis may be exacerbated by this stretch. If your dog has these diagnoses or shows signs of pain anywhere along the spine, consult your veterinarian for stretch recommendations.

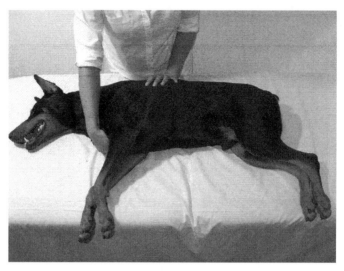

Photo 7.21. Stabilization: *Place one hand firmly on the thoracic spine. Place the other hand firmly on the ribs just beneath the forearms.*

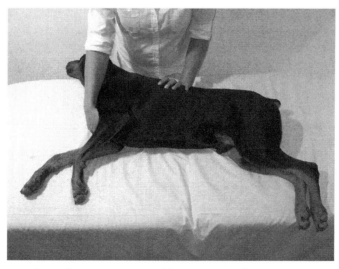

Photo 7.22. Stretch: *Maintain a stable pressure at the spine as you gently pull the ribs toward your body. Hold for 30 seconds.*

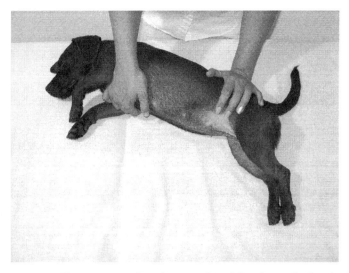

Photo 7.23. Small Dog Stretch: *Place one hand firmly on the low back and pelvis. Place the other hand on the ribs. Gently pull the ribs toward you as you maintain the stablizing pressure.*

Back Rotation/Hip Adduction

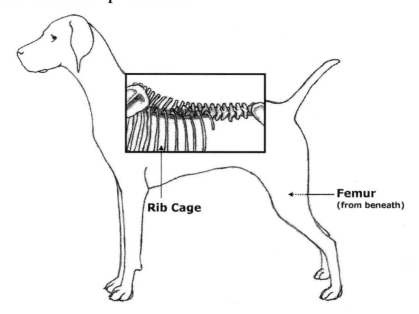

Illustration 7.15. Stabilization: *Rib Cage and Femur (from beneath).*

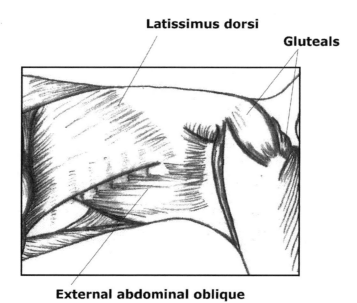

Illustration 7.16. Muscles Stretched: *Latissimus dorsi, External abdominal oblique, Gluteals.*

This stretch can be particularly difficult on some dogs. The most common reasons for the difficulty include a tight Gluteals muscle group, tight low back muscles, and discomfort with positioning. Of all the stretches, this movement is the most foreign to the dog. Initially they need to be taught how to remain relaxed with your arm *under* their hip. You may need to approach this stretch slowly over time until the dog understands that this will make those tight muscles feel better.

Please refrain from stretching the lateral hip if your dog has hip dysplasia, lumbosacral instability, disc diseases, opondylosis, or exhibits pain in the **Attention!** low back. Please consult with your veterinarian prior to stretching.

A Stretch Question

Q: Why is the hip adduction stretch found in the spine section of the book?

A: The hip adductors are the Gluteal muscle group. In side lying, in order to get enough range of motion to stretch the hip abductors, the dog would have to be positioned with his legs off the back of the table. We feel this position is not safe for the dog or the handler. During the spine rotation stretch, the hip abductors are naturally stretched as well as the low back muscles.

Photo 7.24. Stabilization: *Place your hand on top of the mid ribs, gently pressing the ribs down towards the table. Place the other hand beneath the hip on the table and grasp the femur firmly above the stifle.*

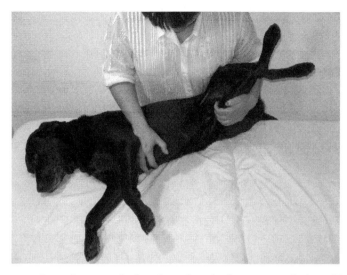

Photo 7.25. Stretch: *Press the hand on the ribs down towards the table as you twist the hind limbs up towards the ceiling. Continue until you feel slight resistance. Hold for 30 seconds.*

Photo 7.26. Small dog stretch: *For smaller dogs you will use just your hands for stabilization and stretch.*

Chapter 8
MAINTENANCE STRETCHING ROUTINES

Once you have mastered the detailed stabilizations, straight planes, and stretches in the previous chapter, you are ready to integrate full-body maintenance stretching routines into the ongoing care of your dog. We recommend that you utilize these maintenance routines two to three times a week (or as your veterinarian recommends) with your dog, more often with an active dog, less often with an inactive dog.

The stretches in the routines are sequenced as they are in the previous chapters, but you can perform the stretches in any order you like. There is no wrong sequence. You might stretch the neck, then the hind limb, the forelimb, and then the spine. I generally stretch whatever body part my dog brings to me first (which depends on how he positions himself on the stretch mat), but I always complete all the stretches. Since so many of the muscles cross more than one joint, stretching all the joints ensures each muscle is stretched appropriately.

The purpose of the maintenance stretching routines is to simplify the stretches so they can be completed with effortlessness and efficiency wherever you may be with your dog. You will notice that for each of the joints, only one joint stabilization is required. This was done intentionally to allow the stretches to flow from one to another with ease. You will also notice that once you have lifted the limb into a straight plane, you can maintain that same straight plane throughout all of the stretches for that particular joint.

Please note the following precautions:

- All dogs must be cleared by their veterinarian prior to beginning a stretching routine.

- If your dog has, or if you suspect your dog may have, any of the following: hip/elbow dysplasia, patellar luxation, cruciate injury, behavioral concerns, pain, is less than 18 months old, is on medication, or has an acute injury, do not stretch your dog before consulting your veterinarian.

- Page references for details on each stretch from earlier chapters are provided within the routines. For the safety of your dog, please refer to these instructions prior to stretching.

Routines for the Healthy Young to Middle Aged Dog

Shoulder Stretches

See Chapter 5, Photos 5.1-5.16 for detailed instructions for the following shoulder stretches.

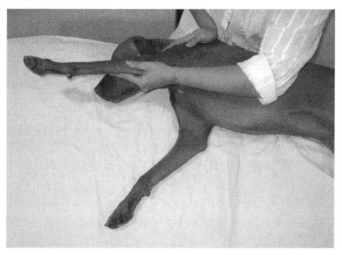

Photo 8.1. Shoulder Flexion. *See pages 59 and 61.*

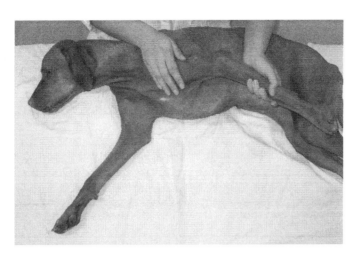

Photo 8.2. Shoulder Extension. *See pages 62-64.*

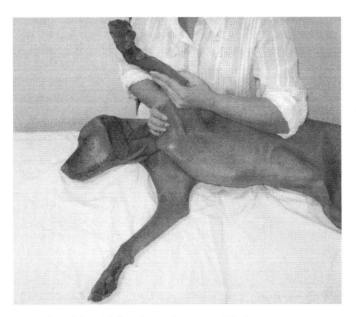

Photo 8.3A. Shoulder Abduction. *See pages 65-69.*

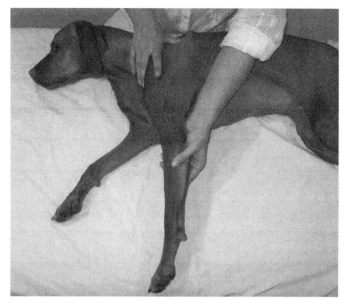

Photo 8.3B. Shoulder Adduction. *See pages 70-72.*

Foreleg Stretches
See Chapter 5, Photos 5.17-5.26 for detailed instructions for the following foreleg stretches.

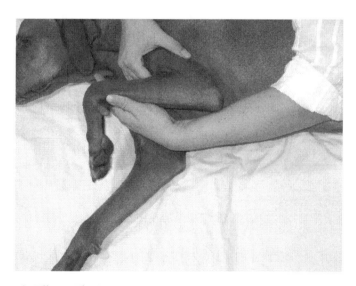

Photo 8.4. Elbow Flexion. *See pages 73-76.*

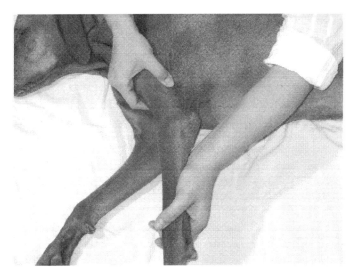

Photo 8.5. Elbow Extension. *See pages 73-76.*

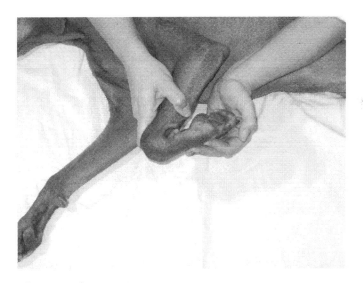

Photo 8.6. Wrist Flexion. *See pages 77-79.*

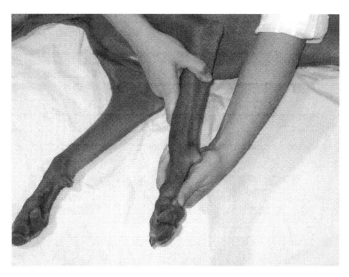

Photo 8.7. Wrist Extension. *See pages 77-79.*

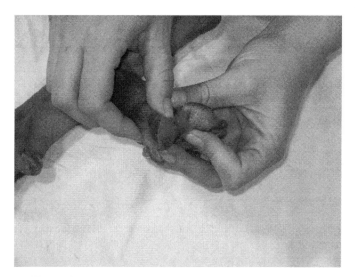

Photo 8.8. Foot. *See pages 80-82.*

Hip Stretches

See Chapter 6, Photos 6.1-6.14 for detailed instructions for the following hip stretches.

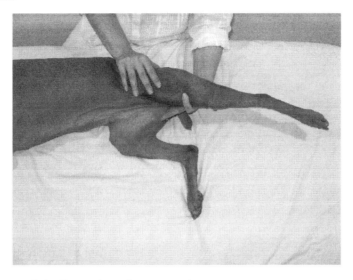

Photo 8.9. Hip Extension. *See pages 85-87.*

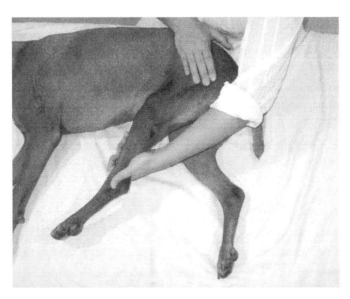

Photo 8.10. Hip Flexion, straight leg. *See pages 88-91.*

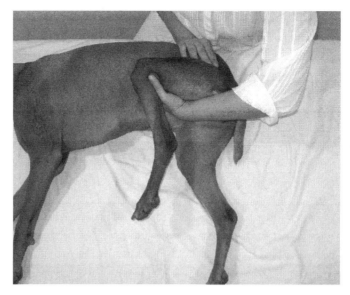

Photo 8.11. Hip Flexion, bent leg. *See pages 88-91.*

Hind Leg Stretches
See Chapter 6, Photos 6.15A-6.21 for detailed stifle instructions. Further hind leg instructions are found in Photos 6.22-6.25.

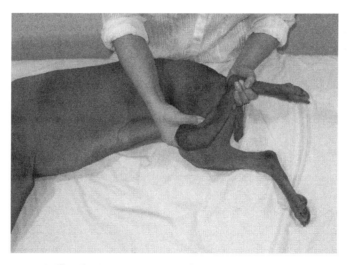

Photos 8.12. Stifle Flexion. *See pages 96-102.*

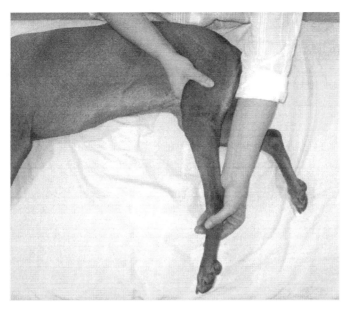

Photo 8.13. Stifle Extension. *See pages 96-102.*

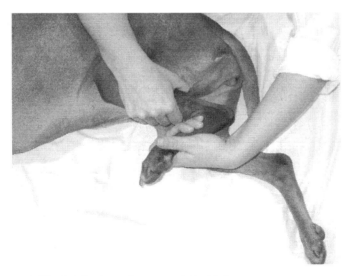

Photo 8.14. Hock Flexion. *See pages 103-106.*

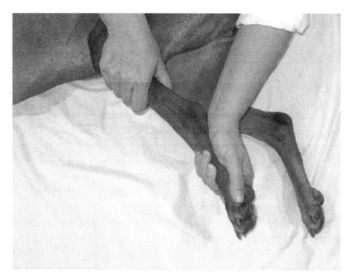

Photo 8.15. Hock Extension. *See pages 103-106.*

Neck and Back Stretches

See Chapter 7, Photos 7.1-7.26 for detailed instructions for the following neck and back stretches.

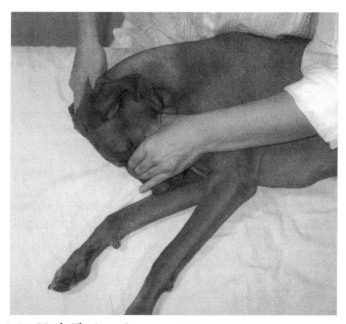

Photo 8.17. Neck Flexion. *See pages 110-112.*

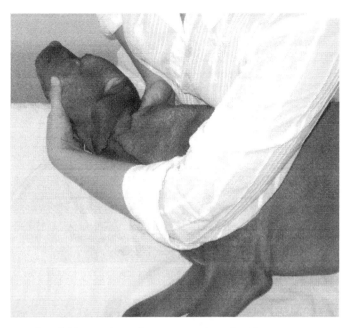

Photo 8.18. Neck Extension. *See pages 113 and 115.*

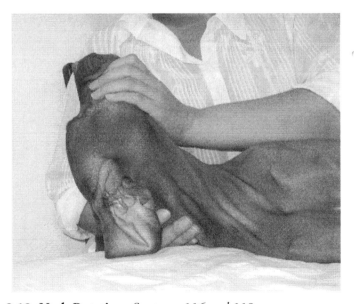

Photo 8.19. Neck Rotation. *See pages 116 and 118.*

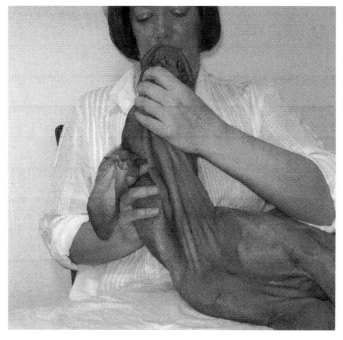

Photo 8.20. Neck Side Bending. *See pages 119-121.*

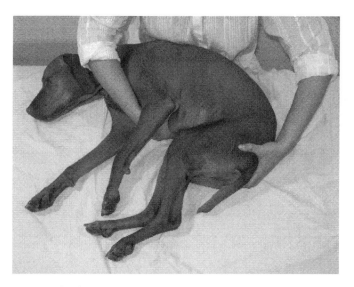

Photo 8.21. Back Flexion. *See pages 123-126.*

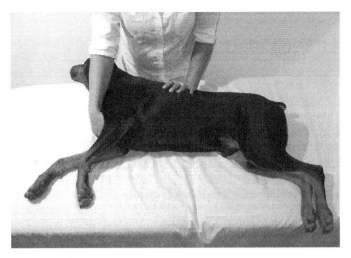

Photo 8.22A. Back Extension. *See pages 127-129.*

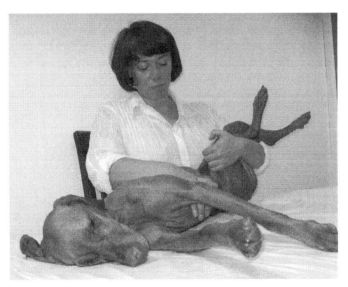

Photo 8.22B. Back Rotation. *See pages 130-132.*

Routines for the Older Dog

The importance of stretching your older dog cannot be overstated. Older dogs lose elasticity in their muscles and are prone to degenerative joint diseases like arthritis. Over time, if inelastic muscles are not stretched, they can form contractures. Contractures occur when the muscle loses all its elasticity and the joint stays in a tightened position. This condition is extremely painful and once a contracture is formed, is it almost impossible to return the joint to normal function. Stretching may prevent this loss of function by keeping the muscles supple for as long as possible.

As recommended above, the sequences of stretches you choose from the options below are up to you and your dog. There is no wrong sequence. But with our old dogs, there is something we can do wrong—we can incorrectly assume that they have more flexibility than they do. Be very aware of the difference in range of motion in an old dog compared to the younger dog. This is why an entire stretching program is recommended when competing with for an old dog.

Remember when stretching, that you should be stretching to the point of feeling resistance, and holding the stretch in that position for 30 seconds. You want the stretch to feel comfortable for your older dog. It is incorrect to think if you stretch them harder, then they will have improved flexibility. It's just the opposite. With old dogs you need to stretch more often, slowly and methodically, carefully holding the stretches at end range. Even if you find a muscle that is tight, you don't want to push past the feeling of slight resistance. Because old dog's muscles lose elasticity, pushing the muscle past the point of slight resistance puts the muscle at risk for tearing. A torn muscle is painful on a younger dog, but in an old dog it can be devastating. The fibers that are not torn have to pick up the work for the portion of the muscle that isn't working. This starts a cascade of events that can cause pain and permanent injury.

So please take special care with your old dog. Move slowly, pay special attention to hand placements and stabilizations, and if you find tight areas, just stretch more frequently, not more aggressively. Your old dog will appreciate your gentle touch.

Notice throughout the following photos that older dogs have less range of motion compared to younger dogs. Since many old dogs have underlying pathologies or injuries, please consult with your veterinarian about developing a stretching routine specific for your older dog.

Shoulder Stretches

Strong joint stabilization and straight plane movement is required for the safety of the shoulder. See Chapter 5, Photos 5.1-5.16 for detailed instructions.

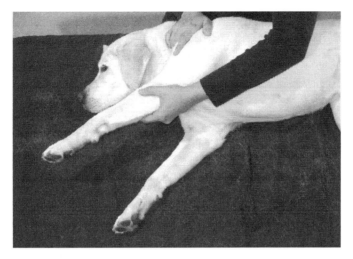

Photo 8.23. Shoulder Flexion. *See pages 59-61.*

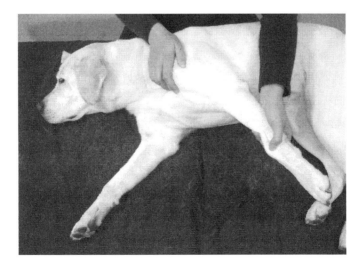

Photo 8.24. Shoulder Extension. *See pages 62-64.*

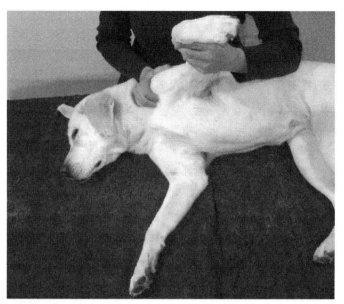

Photo 8.25A. Shoulder Abduction. *See pages 65-69.*

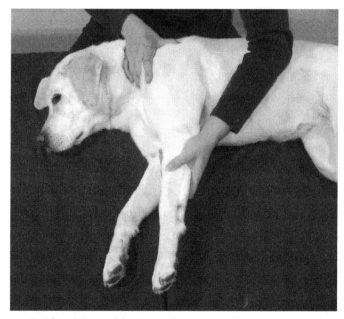

Photo 8.25B. Shoulder Adduction. *See pages 70-72.*

Foreleg Stretches

See Chapter 5, Photos 5.17-5.26 for detailed instructions for the following foreleg stretches.

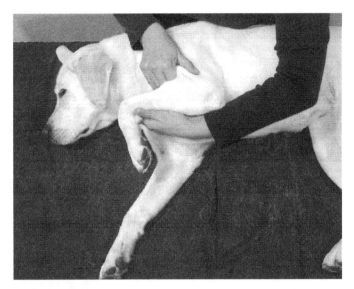

Photo 8.26. Elbow Flexion. *See pages 73-76.*

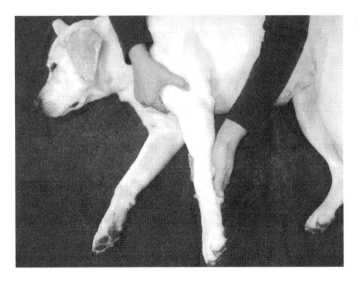

Photo 8.27. Elbow Extension. *See pages 73-76.*

Photo 8.28. Wrist Flexion. *See pages 77-79.*

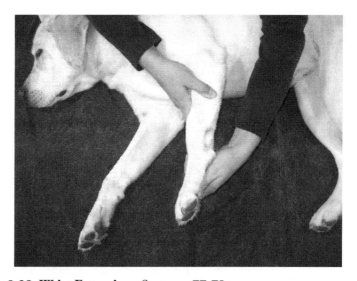

Photo 8.29. Wrist Extension. *See pages 77-79.*

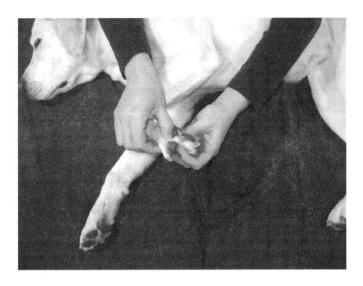

Photo 8.30. Foot. *See pages 80-82.*

Hip Stretches
See Chapter 6, Photos 6.1-6.14 for detailed instructions for the following hip stretches.

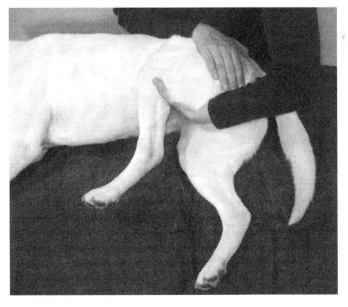

Photo 8.31. Hip Flexion. *See pages 88-91.*

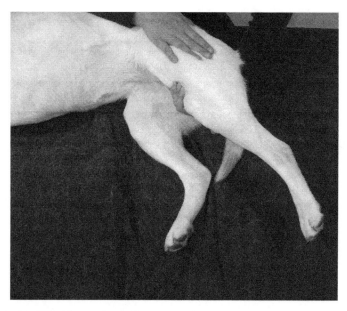

Photo 8.32. Hip Extension. *See pages 85-87.*

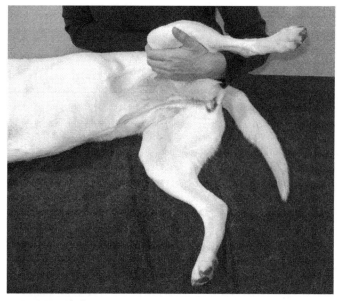

Photo 8.33. Hip Abduction. *See pages 92-95.*

Hind Leg Stretches

See Chapter 6, Photos 6.15A-6.21 for detailed stifle instructions. Further hind leg instructions are found in Photos 6.22-6.25.

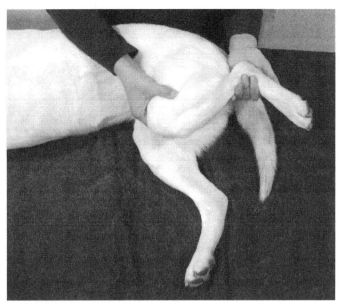

Photo 8.34. Stifle Flexion. *See pages 96-102.*

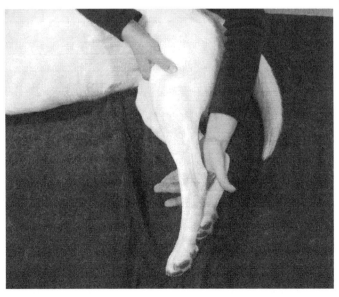

Photo 8.35. Stifle Extension. *See pages 96-102.*

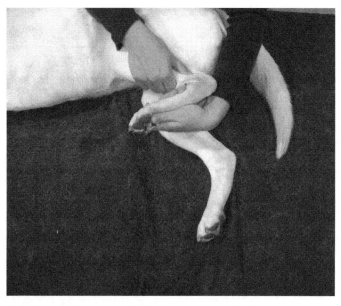

Photo 8.36. Hock Flexion. *See pages 103-106.*

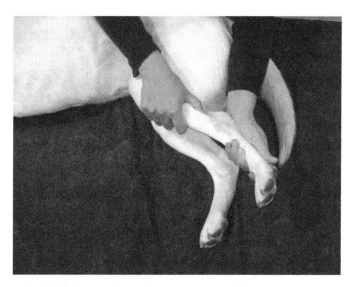

Photo 8.37. Hock Extension. *See pages 103-106.*

Photo 8.38. Foot. *See pages 80-82.*

Neck and Back Stretches
See Chapter 7, Photos 7.1-7.26 for detailed instructions for the following neck and back stretches.

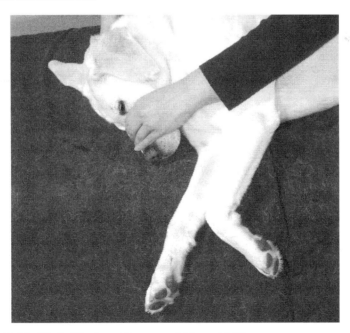

Photo 8.39. Neck Flexion. *See pages 111 and 112.*

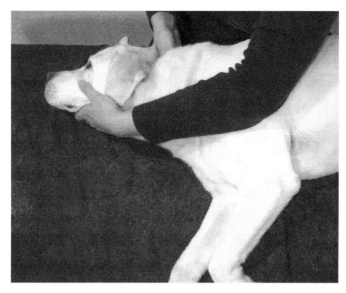

Photo 8.40. Neck Extension. *See pages 113-115.*

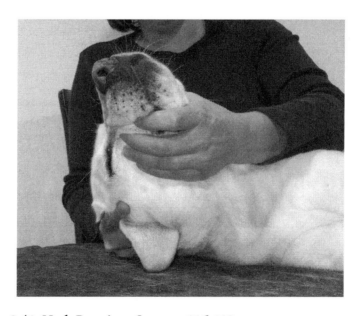

Photo 8.41. Neck Rotation. *See pages 116-118.*

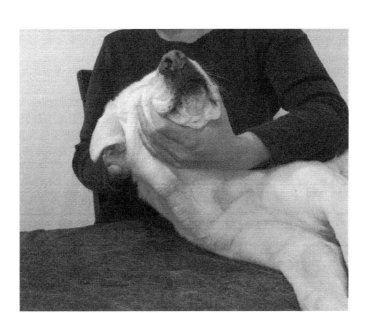

Photo 8.42. Neck Side Bending. *See pages 119-121.*

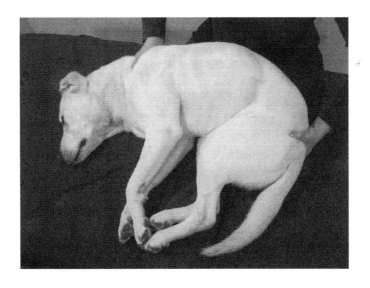

Photo 8.43. Back Flexion. *See pages 123-126.*

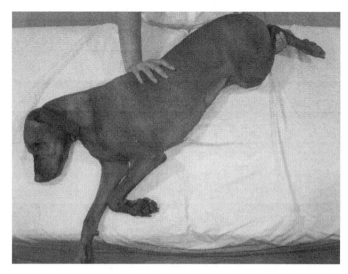

Photo 8.44. Spine Extension. *See pages 127-129.*

Photo 8.45. Back Rotation. *See pages 130-132.*

Chapter 9
SPECIAL ACTIVITY
STRETCHING ROUTINES

Although there is no difference in technique between stretching your pet and your highly active or competition dog, there is a difference in stretching routines. For either type of dog, a maintenance stretching routine will be of great benefit for the overall health and wellness of the muscles and joints. But for the highly competitive canine, additional "activity specific" stretches are highly recommended.

There has been a great deal of research on "specificity of training"—the muscles that perform a specified movement must be trained to do exactly the type of movement that is needed.[1, 2, 3] For example, a long distance runner will want to increase his capacity by running longer and longer distances. But he must also *stretch the muscles* used when increasing his running distance. Why? The purpose of training a muscle is to optimize movement. Only by intentionally overworking a muscle will it gain strength. However, all this overwork will shorten the muscle fibers, predisposing the muscle to injury.

[1]Stegeman, J. (translated by J. S. Skinner): *Exercise physiology.* Year Book Medical Publishers. 1981.

[2]Beneke, R., Hofmann, C., Strauss, N., Hartwig, F., Hoffmann, K., & Behn, C.: "Maximal lactate steady state depends on sports discipline." *Medicine and Science in Sports and Exercise,* 25(5), Supplement abstract 365, 1993.

[3]Bell, G. J., Petersen, S. R., Quinney, A. H., & Wenger, H. A.: "The effect of velocity-specific strength training on peak torque and anaerobic rowing power." *Journal of Sports Sciences,* 7: 205-214, 1989.

Stretching is required to allow the muscle to reach its normal length thereby preventing injuries and improving the quality of the contraction when the muscle works again.

Dogs that participate in specific activities are prone to overworking certain muscle groups and increasing the predisposition for injury in those areas. These muscle groups require specific stretches for injury prevention. It is recommended that all dogs receive a maintenance stretching routine and it is further recommended that active dogs complete a special activity routine to ensure those overworked activity specific muscles are getting the much needed stretching attention they deserve.

Page references for more details on each stretch are provided for each routine. For the safety of your dog. Please refer to these instructions prior to stretching.

Agility Routines

Agility requires three primary types of movements—quick navigational movements to negotiate weave poles and tight turns, absorption of landing forces from jumps, and descent control on the contact obstacles. These movements require increased muscle contraction and control of the forelimbs as well as strong flexion, extension, and rotational forces of the spine. For the agility dog, emphasis on maintaining muscle length in the cranial and caudal forelimb as well as lengthening the tissues of the neck and spine will help optimize these movements and prevent injuries. Stretching the forelimb and the spine after the dog has warmed up and before competition as well as stretching after competition is recommended for optimal health of the joints of the forelimb. See Chapter 5, Photos 5.1-5.16 for detailed instructions on the following stretches.

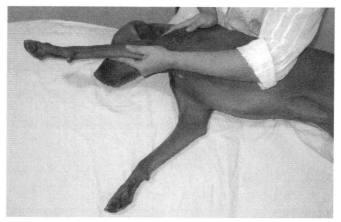

Photo 9.1. Shoulder Flexion. *See pages 59-61.*

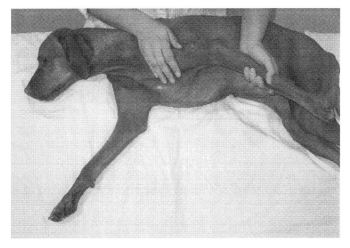

Photo 9.2. Shoulder Extension. *See pages 62-64.*

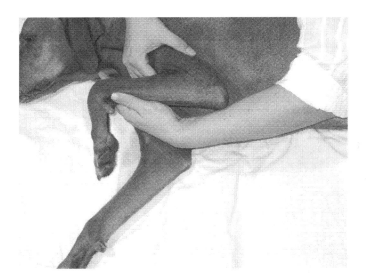

Photo 9.3. Elbow Flexion. *See pages 73-76.*

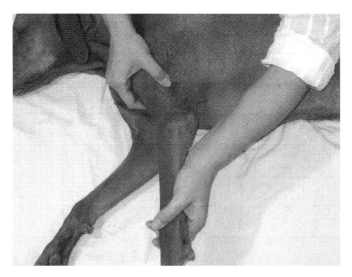

Photo 9.4. Elbow Extension. *See pages 73-76.*

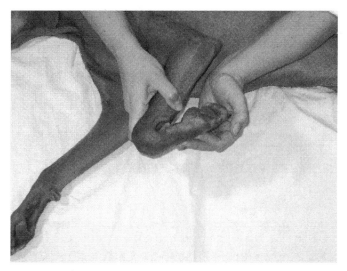

Photo 9.5. Wrist Flexion. *See pages 77-79.*

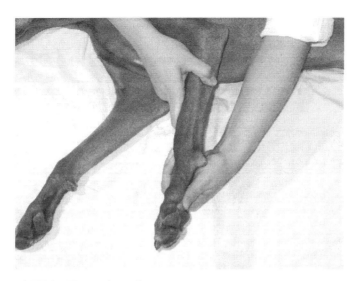

Photo 9.6. Wrist Extension. *See pages 77-79.*

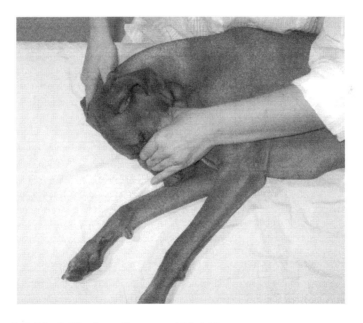

Photo 9.7. Neck Flexion. *See pages 110-112.*

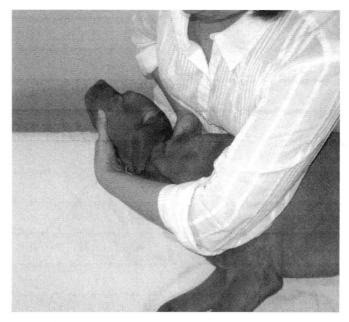

Photo 9.8. Neck Extension. *See pages 113-115.*

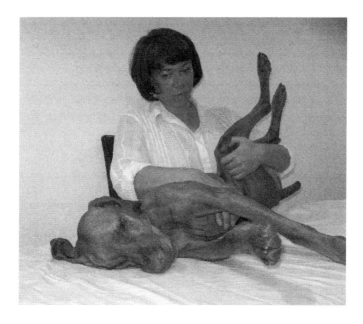

Photo 9.9. Back Rotation. *See pages 130-132.*

Conformation Routines

Conformation requires three important movements from our dogs – forelimb reach, hindlimb drive, and smooth deceleration into a solid stance. The quality of these movements can be optimized by lengthening the muscles on the cranial aspect of the forelimb and hindlimb. By maintaining muscle length and joint integrity in these areas, more fluid movement may be achieved. Muscle length also maintains the integrity of the muscle contraction allowing for a solid "free stack." Stretching for conformation is recommended on a daily basis to keep muscles long and supple and the day of the event (after a warm-up) to ensure fluid movement in the ring. See Chapter 5, Photos 5.1-5.16 for detailed instructions for the following forelimb stretches. See Chapter 6, Photos 6.1-6.14 for detailed instructions for the following hind limb.

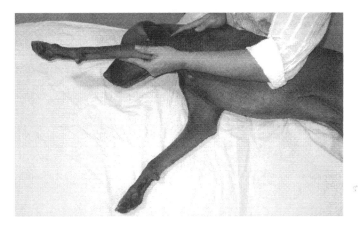

Photo 9.10. Shoulder Flexion. *See pages 59-61.*

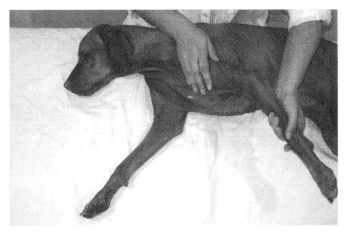

Photo 9.11. Shoulder Extension. *See pages 62-64.*

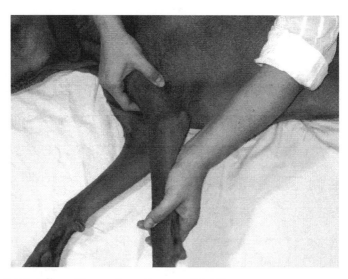

Photo 9.12. Elbow Extension. *See page 73-76.*

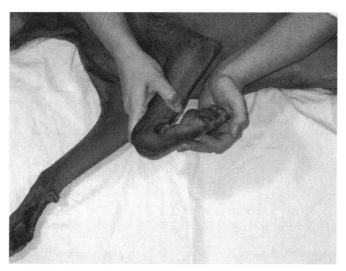

Photo 9.13. Wrist Flexion. *See page 77-79.*

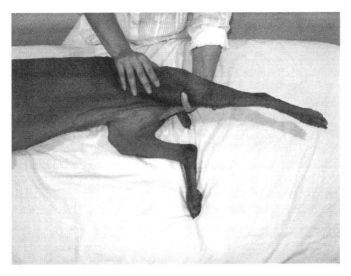

Photo 9.14. Hip Extension. *See page 85-87.*

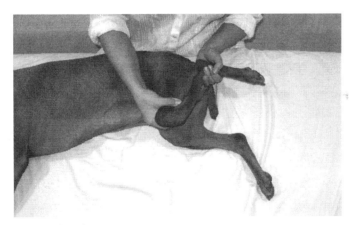

Photo 9.15. Stifle Flexion. *See pages 96-102.*

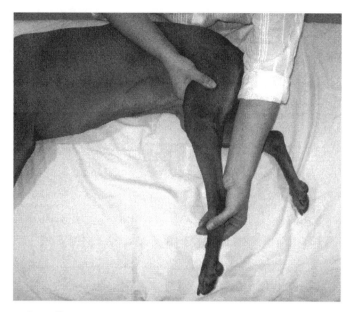

Photo 9.16. Stifle Extension. *See page 96-102.*

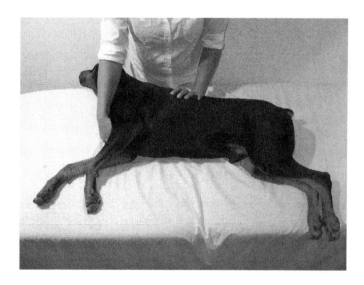

Photo 9.17. Spine Extension. *See pages 127-129.*

Rally and Obedience Routines

Rally and obedience requires some unique movements from our dogs, most specifically a dog's constant attention on his or her handler while sitting, standing, and heeling. This position of attention requires the neck to be in an extended position throughout the session while allowing the rest of the body to move with fluidity. This extended position is difficult for most dogs, but can be exceptionally difficult for small breeds that must hold a very high head position. Maintaining length in the muscles that allow for neck and spine extension will optimize a dog's ability to hold attention (it is easier to maintain attention when there is no pull or strain on the muscles) and will allow for ease of movement in the rest of the body. Stretching for rally and obedience is recommended on a daily basis to maintain muscle length and then, after a warm-up, just prior to the event to ensure necessary flexibility for optimal performance. See Chapter 5, Photos 5.1-5.16, for detailed instructions for forelimb stretches. See Chapter 6, Photos 6.1-6.14, for detailed instructions for hind limb stretches.

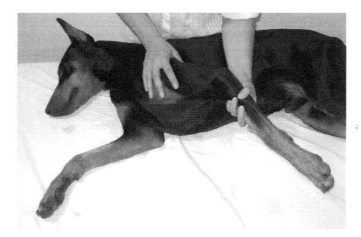

Photo 9.17. Shoulder Extension. *See pages 62-64.*

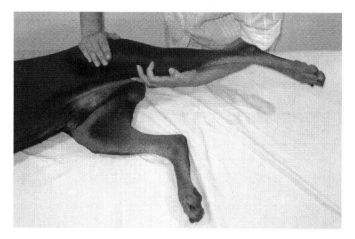

Photo 9.18. Hip Extension. *See pages 85-87.*

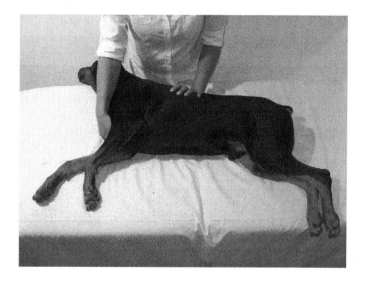

Photo 9.19. Back Extension. *See pages 127-129.*

Photo 9.20. Neck Extension. *See pages 113-115.*

Sled and Weight Pulling Routines

Much of the power required for pulling a snow or weight sled comes from a dog's hind limb and chest muscles. The large and powerful muscles on the back of the leg drive their movement forward as the stomach muscles and chest muscles assist with pulling the weight. Although there is a difference in the types of muscle fibers recruited for long distance sled pulling versus short distance weight pulling, the muscles used in both cases are the same. These powerful dogs will naturally have less flexibility since muscle cells that are designed to create power are shorter and thicker than endurance muscle cells. To optimize movement and prevent injuries in these powerful animals, stretching the muscles that create pull power—the cranial forelimb and hind limb as well as the chest, should be lengthened. Stretching for pulling activities is recommended on a daily basis to maintain flexibility and then immediately following an event to assist with injury prevention. See Chapter 5, Photos 5.1-5.16 for detailed instructions for fore limb stretches. See Chapter 6, Photos 6.1-6.14 for detailed instructions for hind limb stretches.

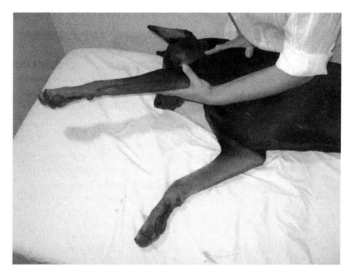

Photo 9.21. Shoulder Flexion. *See pages 59-61.*

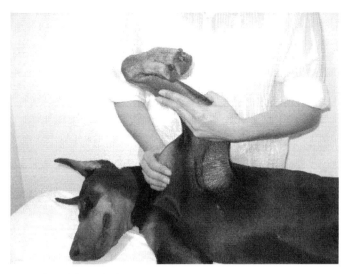

Photo 9.22. Shoulder Abduction. *See page 65-69.*

Photo 9.23. Hip Flexion. *See pages 88-91.*

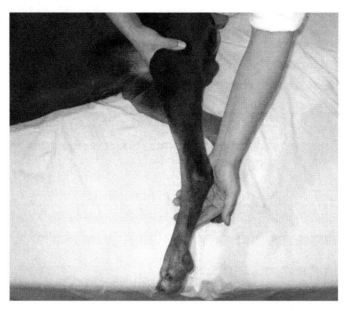

Photo 9.24. Stifle Extension. *See pages 96-102.*

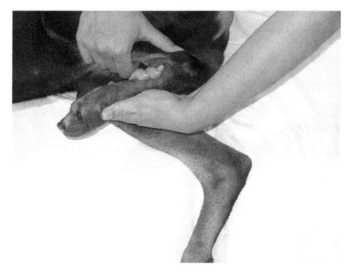

Photo 9.25. Hock Flexion. *See pages 103-106.*

Lure Coursing and Field Work Routines

Lure coursing and field work require fast acceleration and deceleration, quick turns, and endurance. These movements require the entire body to work systematically to propel the dog towards its catch. The muscles on the caudal portion of the hind and forelimbs provide the propulsion for long distance running and the spine, forelimb, and hindlimb provide the movements necessary for quick turns. Keeping these muscles long and supple with stretching will ensure they maintain muscle length for healthy muscle contractions which will streamline movement. For hunting breeds scenting places additional stresses on the neck muscles. Stretching the cranial and lateral neck muscles will help prevent injuries. Stretching for lure coursing and field work is recommended on a daily basis to maintain flexibility and then immediately following an event to assist with injury prevention. See Chapter 5, Photos 5.1-5.16 and Chapter 6, Photos 6.1-6.14 for detailed instructions.

Photo 9.26. Shoulder Flexion. *See pages 59-61.*

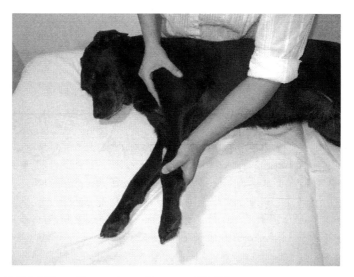

Photo 9.27. Elbow Extension. *See pages 73-76.*

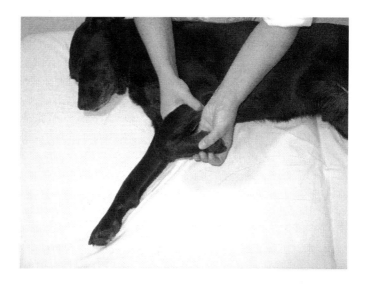

Photo 9.28. Wrist Flexion. *See pages 77-79.*

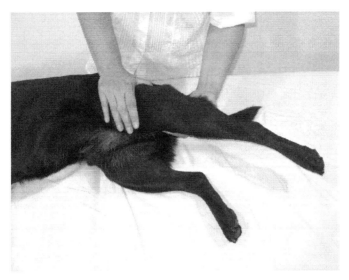

Photo 9.29. Hip Extension. *See page 85-87.*

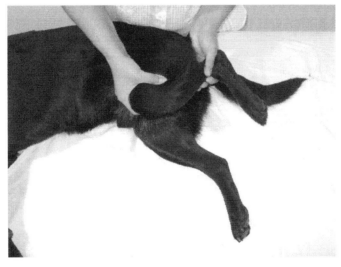

Photo 9.30. Stifle Flexion. *See pages 96-102.*

Photos 9.31. Neck Extension. *See pages 113-115.*

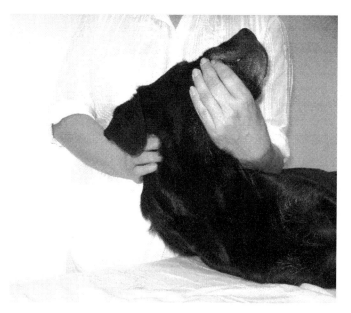

Photo 9.32. Neck Side Bending. *See pages 119-121.*

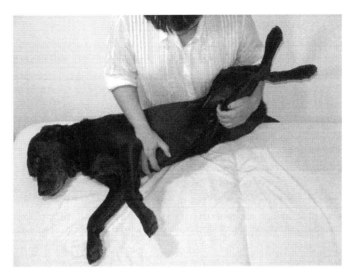

Photo 9.33. Back Rotation. *See pages 130-132.*

Tracking and Search and Rescue Routines

Tracking and rescue requires a prolonged steady gait with the neck extended forward for scenting. This prolonged position places stresses on the shoulder, elbows, wrists, stifles, and hocks. The muscles used to maintain this position for extended periods of time can become fatigued, placing the muscle tissues at risk for shortening injuries. Stretching can lengthen the muscle tissues back to their natural elongated positions preventing injuries and optimizing performance. Special care in the form of regular stretching routines should be given to high drive dogs that may overexert themselves in order to get their find. Stretching is recommended on a daily basis and after a tracking or rescue session.

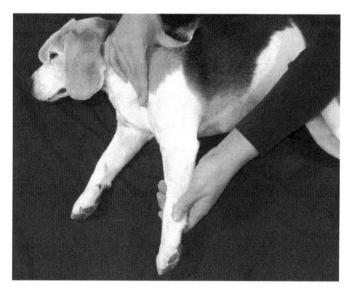

Photo 9.34. Shoulder Adduction. *See pages 70-72.*

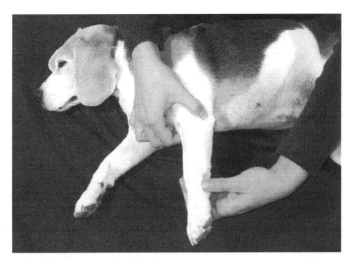

Photo 9.35. Elbow Extension. *See pages 73-76.*

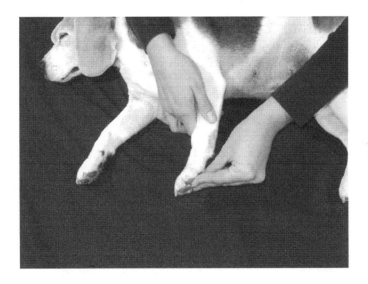

Photo 9.36. Wrist Extension. *See pages 77-79.*

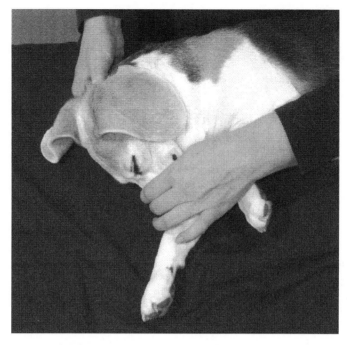

Photo 9.37. Neck Flexion. *See pages 110-112.*

Photo 9.38. Neck Extension. *See pages 113-115.*

Photo 9.39. Back Flexion. *See pages 123-126.*

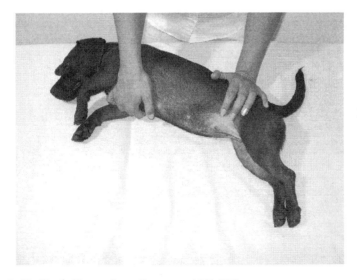

Photo 9.40. Back Extension. *See pages 127-129.*

Disk and Fly Ball Routines

Disk and flyball require repetitive sprinting, jumping, and turning movements at high speeds. The repetitive nature of these movements puts the muscles that create these movements: the hip muscles, neck muscle, spine muscles, and abdominal muscles, at risk for shortening injuries. Maintaining flexibility in these areas with consistent stretching routines will help to prevent repetitive movement injuries. Because healthy muscle tissue can improve the rate of muscle contraction, lengthening muscle tissue can also help to optimize speed and maneuverability for improved performance. Stretching for disk and fly ball is recommended on a daily basis to maintain flexibility. See Chapter 6, Photos 6.1-6.14 for detailed instructions.

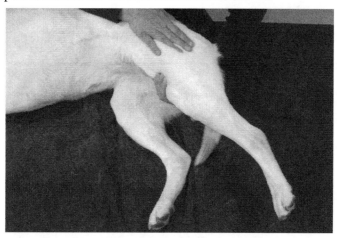

Photo 9.41. Hip Extension. *See pages 85-87.*

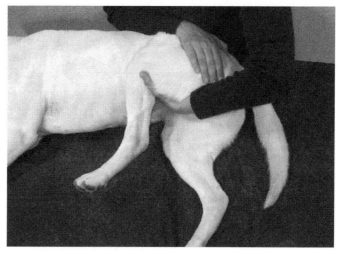

Photo 9.42. Hip Flexion. *See pages 88-91.*

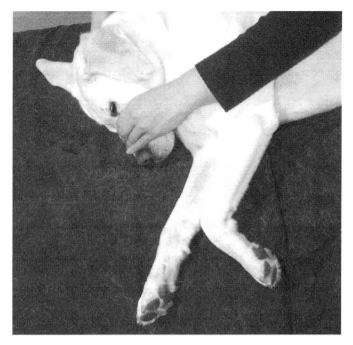

Photo 9.43. Neck Flexion. *See pages 110-112.*

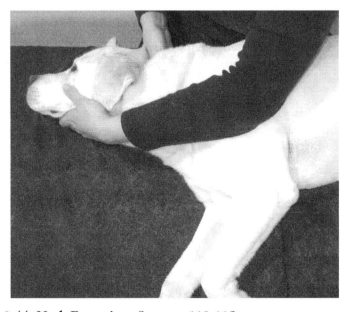

Photo 9.44. Neck Extension. *See pages 113-115.*

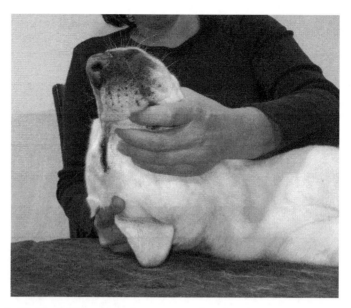

Photo 9.45. Neck Rotation. *See pages 116-118.*

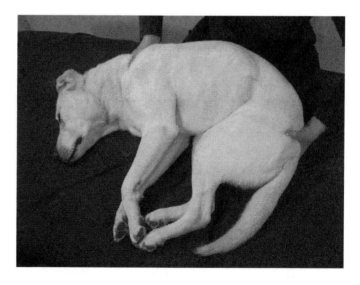

Photo 9.46. Back Flexion. *See pages 123-126.*

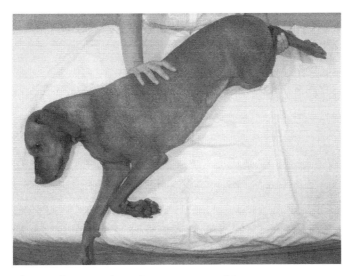

Photo 9.47. Back Extension. *See pages 127-129.*

Photo 9.48. Back Rotation. *See pages 130-132.*

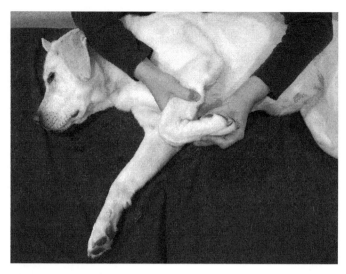

Photo 9.49A. Carpus Flexion. *See pages 77-79.*

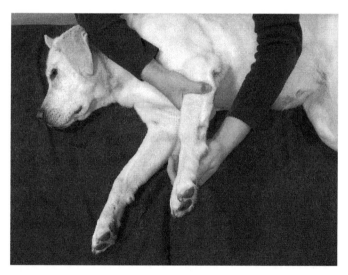

Photo 9.49B. Carpus Extension. *See pages 77-79.*

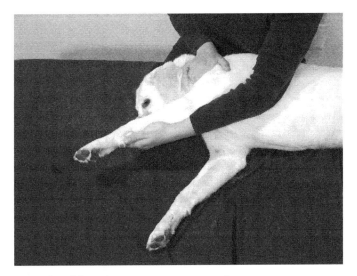

Photo 9.50. Shoulder Flexion. *See pages 59-61.*

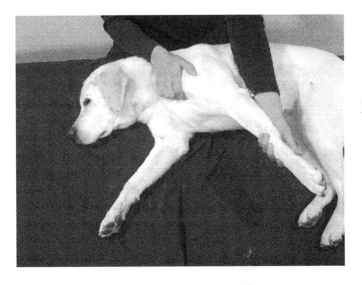

Photo 9.51. Shoulder Extension. *See pages 62-64.*

TERMINOLOGY

Abduction—movement away from midline.

Adduction—movement towards midline.

Articular cartilage—the cartilage that lines joint surfaces.

Ball and socket joint—joint has movement through a rotational range.

Caudal—toward the tail.

Concentric contraction—muscle shortens as it contracts.

Concussive forces—forces created from quick or sudden movements.

Confident grasp—applying a manual stabilization of the joint by holding the joint firmly.

Contact comfort—training the dog to remain relaxed while being touched.

Cranial—toward the head.

Distal—away from the body.

Dorsal—toward the spine.

Dysplasia—abnormal development of tissues, in canines, most commonly seen in the hips and elbow joints.

Eccentric contraction—muscle lengthens as it contracts.

Extension—increasing the angle at a joint.

Flexion—decreasing the angle at a joint.

Golgi Tendon Organ—sensory receptors in the tendon that send nerve messages to the spinal cord when a muscle is contracted.

Hand placement—putting the hands over the correct bones, muscles, and joints in preparation for a stretch.

Hinge joint—joint that moves in only two directions, flexion and extension.

Isometric contraction—muscle length remains the same as it contracts.

Lateral—away from midline.

Lumbar lordosis—in humans, natural curve of the low back.

Medial—towards midline.

Muscles—bundles of contracting fibers bound together by connective tissues to allow them to work in conjunction with each other to create movement.

Muscle cells (fibers)—the smallest contractile unit of a muscle.

Muscle spindle cell—sensory receptors in the muscle tissue that send nerve messages to the spinal cord when the muscle is lengthened (stretched).

Myofilaments—the smallest contractile unit of a muscle.

Proprioception—nerve sensations that provide information about the position and movement of the body in space. This sensory response is vitally important for balance, movement, and navigating uneven terrain.

Proximal—towards the body.

Relaxation—muscle tissue is not contracting.

Rostral—towards the nose in reference to the head of the dog.

Rotation—movement around a central axis.

Stabilization—manual support of the joint.

Straight plane movement—lifting the long bones of the limb into alignment with the joint being stretched ensuring correct movement through the joint.

Stretch—passive elongation of elastic and non elastic muscle fibers.

Stretch reflex—contraction of muscle fibers that is mediated by sensory receptors when a muscle is lengthened.

Tendon—specialized connective tissue that connects a bone to a muscle.

Three-to-Five Second Rule—counting three to five seconds from the starting position of the limb to the limb stretching position.

Ventral—towards the abdomen.

Viscous—resistance to movement of fluid.

Warming—increasing blood flow to muscle tissue thereby decreasing viscosity of the tissue.

RECOMMENDED READING

Brown, Curtis. *Dog Locomotion and Gait Analysis.* 1986, Hoflin.

Clothier, Suzanne. *Your Athletic Dog, A Functional Approach* (video and workbook). 1995, Flying Dog Press.

Colville, Thomas, and Bassert, Joanna. *Clinical Anatomy & Physiology for Veterinary Technicians.* 2002, Mosby.

Edwards, Brian. *Comparative Anatomy of the Dog* (Flash Cards). 1996.

Elliot, Rachel Page. *Dogsteps, A New Look.* 2001, Doral Publishing.

Elliott, Rachel Page. *Dogsteps, What to Look for in a Dog* (DVD). 1986, Dogwise Publishing.

Evans, Howard, and DeLahunta, Alexander. *Miller's Guide to the Dissection of the Dog, 4th ed.* 1996, W.B. Saunders.

Hourdebaigt, Jean Pierre LMT. *Canine Massage, A Complete Reference Manual.* 2004, Dogwise Publishing.

Kandel, Eric; Schwartz, James; and Jessell, Thomas. *Principles of Neural Science, 3rd ed.* 1991, Appleton & Lange.

Nordin, Margareta and Frankel, Victor. *Basic Biomechanics of the Musculoskeletal System.* 1989, Lippincott Williams & Wilkins.

Pasquini, Chris; Spurgeon, Tom; and Pasquini, Susan. *Anatomy of Domestic Animals, Systemic and Regional Approach.* 1995, Sudz Publishing.

Rugaas, Turid. *Calming Signals, What Your Dog Tells You.* 2000, Dogwise Publishing.

Spira, Harold. *Canine Terminology.* 1982, Dogwise Publishing.

Summers, Alleice. *Common Diseases of Companion Animals.* 2002, Mosby.

AUTHORS AND MODELS

Sasha Foster is a physical therapist, yoga instructor, and writer whose passion is geriatric advocacy (in any species). She has her Master's Degree in Physical Therapy and is pursuing her canine physical therapist certification. She has completed numerous research projects ranging from cellular neurology to geriatric weight training and is currently developing an exercise DVD for individuals with muscular dystrophies. She looks

forward to further development of *The Healthy Way to Stretch Your Dog* including a stretching DVD and further studies that will lead to stretching for movement optimization. In addition, she and her dog, Quin, have provided Animal-Assisted Therapy to geriatric rehabilitation populations throughout Colorado.

Ashley Foster is a Certified Pet Dog Trainer with 13 years of experience whose passion is reward based training and canine advocacy. She has a Bachelor's of Science Degree in Zoology and is pursuing her certificate in Canine Behavior Consulting. She specializes in training and behavior modification in dogs with severe behavioral problems ranging from separation anxiety to aggression. In addition, Ashley handles multiple breeds in conformation for AKC events throughout the United States while being an owner/handler for her own Doberman Pinschers in conformation, obedience, and rally. She looks forward to further development of *The Healthy Way to Stretch Your Dog* knowing that it can help improve the quality of life for dogs and improve the canine-human relationship.

Featured Dog Models

Savannah
Name: Ch Titan-N-
Dotsero's Sugar Magnolia
RN, JH, OA, OAJ

Breed: Vizsla

Age: 6 years

Activities: Agility, Rally,
Obedience, Training for
Senior Hunter

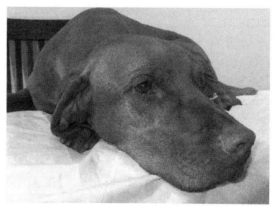

Response to Stretching:
lengthened tight hip and chest muscles for improved jumping and turning in agility

Owned and loved by: Ginger and Gary Sammonds

Aspen
Name: Aspen

Breed: Labrador

Age: 9 years

Activities: high mountain
hiking (several Colorado
14ers), marathon training,
snow shoeing

Response to Stretching:
decreased overall tightness
due to high activity levels, the following morning slept two hours longer than usual

Owned and loved by: Helen and Chris Holmquist-Johnson

Puzzle

Name: Ch Yrissari S'More's Puzzle

Breed: 13" Beagle

Age: 8 years

Activities: Conformation, camping, hiking, fishing

Response to Stretching: decreased chest and hip tightness, increased energy after stretching

Owned and loved by: Karlene Brumfield

Quin

Name: Quin, rescue dog

Breed: Labrador

Age: 7 years

Activities: Obedience, Animal Assisted Therapy, three mile daily walks

Primary Response to Stretching: improved shoulder range of motion, assisted with healing biceps tendonitis under veterinarian care

Owned and loved by: Sasha Foster

Diesel

Name: Ch Imagemaker's Crowd-plezer CD, ROM, RA, CGC

Breed: Doberman Pinscher

Age: 5 years

Activities: Conformation, Agility, Obedience, Rally

Response to Stretching: relief of ongoing upper back tightness, improved attention in heeling after neck stretches

Owned and loved by: Ashley Foster

INDEX

VETERINARIAN STRETCH SCREENING FORM

Throughout the book we have described in detail the importance of stretching for injury prevention and movement optimization. We have also brought attention to numerous medical issues that can be exacerbated by stretching. In order to help veterinarians clarify which stretches are safe for us to complete with our dogs and which stretches are not, we have created the Veterinarian Stretch Screening Form. On this form, a photograph of each stretch is provided so your veterinarian can specify if there are any stretches that you should not complete.

This form is available as a downloadable PDF at www.dogwise.com/pdf/stretchform/pdf.

Veterinarian Stretch Screening Form

It is imperative that all dogs be cleared by their veterinarian prior to beginning any stretching program.

Date_____ Dog Name_____

Age_____ Owner Name_____

Phone Number_____ E-mail_____

Stretch		Yes	No	Modify (please specify)
Shoulder Flexion				
Shoulder Extension				
Shoulder Abduction				
Shoulder Adduction				
Elbow Flexion				
Elbow Extension				
Carpus Flexion				
Carpus Extension				

Stretch		Yes	No	Modify (please specify)
Forelimb Foot Flexion/ Extension				
Hip Flexion Straight Leg				
Hip Flexion Bent Leg				
Hip Extension				
Hip Abduction				
Stifle Flexion				
Stifle Extension				
Hock Flexion				
Hock Extension				

Stretch		Yes	No	Modify (please specify)
Hind Limb Foot Flexion/ Extension				
Neck Flexion				
Neck Extension				
Neck Rotation				
Neck Lateral Bend				
Back Flexion				
Back Extension				
Back Rotation (Hip Adduction)				
Other Recommendations:				

Prepared by: _____

From Dogwise Publishing
www.dogwise.com
1-800-776-2665

BEHAVIOR & TRAINING

ABC's of Behavior Shaping. Fundamentals of Training; Proactive Behavior Mgmt, DVD. Ted Turner

Aggression In Dogs. Practical Mgmt, Prevention & Behaviour Modification. Brenda Aloff

Am I Safe? DVD. Sarah Kalnajs

Barking. The Sound of a Language. Turid Rugaas

Behavior Problems in Dogs, 3rd ed. William Campbell

Brenda Aloff's Fundamentals. Foundation Training for Every Dog, DVD. Brenda Aloff

Bringing Light to Shadow. A Dog Trainer's Diary. Pam Dennison

Canine Body Language. A Photographic Guide to the Native Language of Dogs. Brenda Aloff

Changing People Changing Dogs. Positive Solutions for Difficult Dogs. Dee Ganley

Clicked Retriever. Lana Mitchell

Dog Behavior Problems. The Counselor's Handbook. William Campbell

Dog Detectives. Train Your Dog to Find Lost Pets. Kat Albrecht

Dog Friendly Gardens. Garden Friendly Dogs. Cheryl Smith

Dog Language. An Encyclopedia of Canine Behavior. Roger Abrantes

Evolution of Canine Social Behavior, 2nd ed. Roger Abrantes

Fighting Dominance in a Dog Whispering World, DVD. Jean Donaldson and Ian Dunbar

Focus Not Fear. Training Insights from a Reactive Dog Class. Ali Brown

Get Connected With Your Dog, book with DVD. Brenda Aloff

Give Them a Scalpel and They Will Dissect a Kiss, DVD. Ian Dunbar

Guide To Professional Dog Walking And Home Boarding. Dianne Eibner

Language of Dogs, DVD. Sarah Kalnajs

Mastering Variable Surface Tracking, Component Tracking (2 bk set). Ed Presnall

Mindful Dog Teaching. Reflections on the Relationships We Share with our Dogs. Claudeen McAuliffe

My Dog Pulls. What Do I Do? Turid Rugaas

New Knowledge of Dog Behavior (reprint). Clarence Pfaffenberger

Oh Behave! Dogs from Pavlov to Premack to Pinker. Jean Donaldson

On Talking Terms with Dogs. Calming Signals, 2nd edition. Turid Rugaas

On Talking Terms with Dogs. What Your Dog Tells You, DVD. Turid Rugaas

Play With Your Dog. Pat Miller

Positive Perspectives. Love Your Dog, Train Your Dog. Pat Miller

Positive Perspectives 2. Know Your Dog, Train Your Dog. Pat Miller

Predation and Family Dogs, DVD. Jean Donaldson

Really Reliable Recall. Train Your Dog to Come When Called, DVD. Leslie Nelson

Right on Target. Taking Dog Training to a New Level. Mandy Book & Cheryl Smith

Stress in Dogs. Martina Scholz & Clarissa von Reinhardt

Tales of Two Species. Essays on Loving and Living With Dogs. Patricia McConnell

The Dog Trainer's Resource. The APDT Chronicle of the Dog Collection. Mychelle Blake (ed)

The Dog Trainer's Resource 2. The APDT Chronicle of the Dog Collection. Mychelle Blake (ed)

The Language of Dogs, 2 disc DVD set. Sarah Kalnajs

The Thinking Dog. Crossover to Clicker Training. Gail Fisher

Therapy Dogs. Training Your Dog To Reach Others. Kathy Diamond Davis

Training Dogs. A Manual (reprint). Konrad Most

Training the Disaster Search Dog. Shirley Hammond

Try Tracking. The Puppy Tracking Primer. Carolyn Krause

Visiting the Dog Park, Having Fun, and Staying Safe. Cheryl S. Smith

When Pigs Fly. Train Your Impossible Dog. Jane Killion
Winning Team. A Guidebook for Junior Showmanship. Gail Haynes
Working Dogs (reprint). Elliot Humphrey & Lucien Warner

HEALTH & ANATOMY, SHOWING
An Eye for a Dog. Illustrated Guide to Judging Purebred Dogs. Robert Cole
Another Piece of the Puzzle. Puppy Development. Pat Hastings
Annie On Dogs! Ann Rogers Clark
Canine Cineradiography, DVD. Rachel Page Elliott
Canine Massage, A Complete Reference Manual. Jean-Pierre Hourdebaigt
Canine Reproduction and Whelping. A Dog Breeder's Guide. Myra Savant Harris
Canine Terminology (reprint). Harold Spira
Dog Breeders Professional Secrets. Ethical Breeding Practices. Sylvia Smart
Dog In Action (reprint). Macdowell Lyon
Dogsteps DVD. Rachel Page Elliott
Performance Dog Nutrition. Optimize Performance With Nutrition. Jocelynn Jacobs
Positive Training for Show Dogs. Building A Relationship for Success. Vicki Ronchette
Puppy Intensive Care. A Breeder's Guide To Care Of Newborn Puppies. Myra Savant Harris
Raw Dog Food. Make It Easy for You and Your Dog. Carina MacDonald
Raw Meaty Bones. Tom Lonsdale
Shock to the System. The Facts About Animal Vaccination... Catherine O'Driscoll
The History and Management of the Mastiff. Elizabeth Baxter & Pat Hoffman
Tricks of the Trade. From Best Intentions to Best in Show, Rev. Ed. Pat Hastings
What Vets Don't Tell You About Vaccines, 2nd Ed. Catherine O'Driscoll
Whelping Healthy Puppies, DVD. Sylvia Smart
Work Wonders. Feed Your Dog Raw Meaty Bones. Tom Lonsdale

Also available from Dogwise Publishing

Go to www.dogwise.com for more books and ebooks.

Canine Cross Training
Building Balance, Strength and Endurance in Your Dog
Sasha Foster, MSPT, CCRT

When the four conditioning components are executed in a systematic approach using the key exercise principles of frequency, intensity and duration, you can train your dog to reach his fullest potential in whatever canine sport or activity you choose to participate in—and help keep him fitter and more injury-free over a longer period of time.

The Healthy Way to Stretch Your Dog
A Physical Therapy Approach with Activity Specific Stretching Routines DVD
Sasha Foster, MSPT, CCRT and Ashley Foster, CPDT-KA

This DVD demonstrates how to safely and effectively stretch each major muscle group. Teaches correct hand placement for joint stabilization and how to maintain good form. Stretching routines are presented for both large and small dogs, older dogs, and those that are involved in a variety of dog sports.

Canine Massage, 2nd Ed.
A Complete Reference Manual
Jean-Pierre Hourdebaigt, L.M.T.

Bring the well-known benefits of massage to your own dog or become a canine massage specialist. Over 100 illustrations and 100 photos, detailed examinations of muscular stress points, diagnoses, and treatments.

Canine Massage
DVD In 3 Easy Steps DVD
Natalie Lenton

Whether you are a complete novice, or have experience with massage, this DVD is a must for every dog owner who wants to improve or maintain their dog's quality of life, mobility and comfort level. Within one hour, this DVD will give you all the knowledge you need to massage your dog like a professional.

Performance Dog Nutrition
DVD Optimize Performance with Nutrition
Dr. Jocelynn Jacobs

Get better performance from your canine athlete! Learn how to meet the special nutritional needs of your performance dog and how to meet them with a sound nutrition program. Explains how to read dog food labels and select appropriate food for your dog.

From Tongue to Tail
The Integrated Movement of the Dog DVD
Julia Robertson and Liz Pope

By watching this unique DVD, with its slow motion and animation, you will be able to see how a dog moves during day to day activities and the stresses put upon their whole body, whether walking, trotting, running or jumping.

Dogwise.com your source for quality books, ebooks, DVDs, training tools and treats.

We've been selling to the dog fancier for more than 25 years and we carefully screen our products for quality information, safety, durability and FUN! You'll find something for every level of dog enthusiast on our website www.dogwise.com or drop by our store in Wenatchee, Washington.

35354965R00123

Printed in Great Britain
by Amazon